Alzheimer's: Forgetting Piece by Piece

Ami Simms
Curator

ISBN: 978-0-943079-09-7

First Edition. Alzheimer's: Forgetting Piece by Piece

Copyright © 2007 Mallery Press, Inc.

Mallery Press, Inc.
4206 Sheraton Drive
Flint, MI 48532
1-800-278-4824
www.AlzQuilts.org

Graphic Design:
Celia McCulloch

Photography:
Lee Kirchner
Axis Creative

Copy Editors:
Janet Beckstrom
Debbie Chenail
Morna McEver Golletz
Susan Shevrin
Nanette Zeller

Printed in the United States of America
by Malloy, Inc. and University Lithoprinters

Library of Congress Control Number: 2007902529

All profit from the sale of this book will be used to fund Alzheimer's research.

Dedication

For all those who walk in the shadow of Alzheimer's. May future generations never know this disease.

Acknowledgements

You are holding this book in your hands because of the generosity and hard work of the following people to whom I am so very grateful:

- The talented and courageous artists who created the quilts for Alzheimer's: Forgetting Piece by Piece. Through their hands we see their hearts and we are changed.

- Celia McCulloch for the outstanding book design, taking it from concept to pre-press with aplomb.

- Lee Kirchner for the exquisite photography and his unwavering support.

- Patrice Smith and Deb Sulkowski who believed in this project and made it their own.

- Janet Beckstrom, Debbie Chenail, Morna Golletz, Marsha McCloskey, Susan Shevrin, Jennie Simms, and Nanette Zeller. You fill my heart with your kindness.

- For my husband Steve and daughter Jennie: your love and support are the reason I lead a charmed life. I am so thankful. I couldn't do any of this without you; and I wouldn't want to.

- And for Mom, who sometimes still remembers what she'd always tell me before any important undertaking: "Give 'em Hell, Baby!" I miss you.

I look at my mother's face as she watches me come in the door. It will take her a full five seconds to process who I am, and it is an agonizing wait.

"Hi, Mom!"

I'm her only child. She stares at me, unknowing. Her brain is working hard to process what she sees, or what it thinks she sees, and what she heard, or what it thinks she heard. She knows she doesn't know. It is agony for her, too.

Finally, her face changes. Somewhere deep in her brain she has found the memory of me. Her face relaxes, her eyes get brighter, she reaches out to hug me and asks, "How did you find me?!," as if I were searching for her as she had been searching for me.

My mother has Alzheimer's disease. Her brain is dying. She has lost most of her life's memories and life skills. She can't remember that I visited yesterday. She will eventually be unable to find her memory of me at all.

It has been six years since Mom was diagnosed, about seven since she began to notice that something in her mind wasn't right. The disease that is killing her brain cells probably began its dirty work a decade or more before that. Alzheimer's is a long journey of frustration, and heartbreak, and waste.

Through my mother's illness I've seen first hand what Alzheimer's takes and what it leaves behind, swapping understanding for confusion, ability for powerlessness, and the joy of life for loneliness and isolation. I've visited all the stages of grief, but I haven't been very good at letting go of the anger or the sorrow.

The idea for what would become the Alzheimer's Art Quilt Initiative first popped into my head in the shower. When Mom was living with us, it was one of the few places I could let out my tears privately. I took very long showers.

I had already thought of making a quilt to express my anger at the disease and my frustration as a caregiver. It would have lots of black thread, symbolic of the plaques and tangles growing inside my mother's brain. As the water cascaded over me, I again rehearsed quilting it by machine, the needle furiously jamming thread into fabric until nearly all of the patchwork was obscured.

As I shampooed, I wondered if my angry quilt should have company. Surely other quilters would be interested in the artistic challenge of portraying Alzheimer's in fabric. One or two might even have had a family member with the disease. By time I toweled off, the idea had morphed into a full-blown quilt exhibit. Quilts about Alzheimer's would travel coast to coast to raise awareness about this awful disease.

In subsequent showers I ruminated on the success of other quilters who have raised money for worthwhile causes (thank you, Virginia Spiegel), and I mentally added a fund-raising component. A logo and Web site took shape in my mind.

The ideas were delicious, coming faster than I could catch them. The project would be totally grass roots, Internet-driven, and self-funded. It would raise awareness while making money for Alzheimer's research. All profit would be donated. Then, as fast as water pressure drops when somebody upstairs flushes the toilet, I realized there was no way I could even attempt it! I was the primary caregiver for my mom, trying to be a wife and a mother, running a business, and traveling out of state to teach quilting every month. I was already overwhelmed. It would be totally insane to add one more thing to my plate. I'd have to pass on the best idea I'd ever had.

I mourned its demise. I couldn't stop thinking about it. It began to haunt me. Slowly, over a period of several weeks, the thing that I couldn't possibly do became the thing that I couldn't **not** do. Double negative aside, it would be a way to channel the anger and sadness I felt into something positive. Maybe it would make a difference. How could I turn my back on that?

In August of 2005 I began testing the waters, e-mailing other professional quilters to gauge their interest in making a quilt for the traveling exhibit. To my amazement, many of my colleagues knew about Alzheimer's. Some had lost relatives to the disease, others were caring for parents suffering from it, and some just wanted to help. Eighteen quilters committed to the project. Based on their reputations alone I was able to book "Alzheimer's: Forgetting Piece by Piece" in more than half a dozen venues before the quilts were even finished. The rest of the quilts would be juried in, via e-mail, in June 2006.

I was looking for strong visual images with supporting written statements that told the story of Alzheimer's from a variety of perspectives and experiences. Most submissions brought me to tears, instantly. If the quilts didn't, the artists' statements did. I tried to select quilts that represented diversity in focus, technique, and style.

The resulting exhibit includes sad imaginings of an existence stripped of memory and learning; gritty illustrations of the anger, frustration, and stress of care giving; beautiful tributes to loved ones taken by Alzheimer's; and the anticipation of a future cure. These are extraordinary quilts of heartbreak and hope.

"Alzheimer's: Forgetting Piece by Piece" debuted at the American Quilter's Society Quilt Exposition in Nashville, Tennessee in August 2006. It will travel until the end of July 2009, when the quilts will be returned to the artists who made them.

All of the quilts in the exhibit are faithfully reproduced in this book along with the artists' statements. Each artist statement is paired with information about Alzheimer's disease. (For more detailed information, visit the Alzheimer's Association, the leading voluntary health organization in Alzheimer's research and support at www.Alz.org or call 1-800-372-3900.)

My hope is that the quilts on these pages will touch your heart and that what you learn about Alzheimer's disease will prompt you to take action. Empathy and knowledge is a good foundation for advocacy. Through advocacy we will move closer to a cure. You have already helped by purchasing this book. All of the profit, everything except the cost to produce, market, and sell the book, will be donated to Alzheimer's research. (See www.AlzQuilts.org and click on "Show Me the Money" to see the breakdown.) Take the next step and share this book with a friend. Better yet, tell them to buy their own copy. That's more money for research!

The Alzheimer's Art Quilt Initiative also sponsors another project—Priority: Alzheimer's Quilts. You can be a quilt maker and/or a quilt buyer of very small art quilts, no larger than 9 inches by 12 inches. Named for the urgent need to fund research, and because the quilts are shipped to their new owners in USPS priority mailers, the project raises money for Alzheimer's research. Priority: Alzheimer's Quilts are auctioned during the first 10 days of each month at www.AlzQuilts.org or sold outright at select quilting exhibitions throughout the country.

With my sincerest thanks to the quilt artists who have shared their outstanding talent, it is my great pleasure to invite you now to experience "Alzheimer's: Forgetting Piece by Piece."

Grab a tissue,

Ami Simms
Curator, *Alzheimer's: Forgetting Piece by Piece*
Founder, *Alzheimer's Art Quilt Initiative*
www.AlzQuilts.org

Leaving Us

34" x 42"
Cheryl Lynch
Broomall, Pennsylvania

Cheryl made her first quilt in 1975 as a newlywed and impoverished chemistry graduate student. But it took another 17 years for her to make the next one. That second quilt led to a career that has involved teaching, designing Judaic patterns, commissions, and winning ribbons at quilt shows.

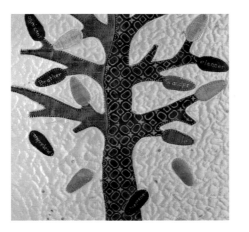

Leaving Us

The slow progression of my dad's Alzheimer's was initially easy to ignore. He lived alone in Florida after my mom died. When he told us he had bugs in his apartment at night and said he was trying to kill them with a hammer, we chose to ignore it. When he phoned our house twelve times a day, we ignored it. When he showed up at his doctor's office several times in one week, we ignored it. When his landlord told us his lease couldn't be renewed because of his behavior, we could no longer ignore it.

Dad lost his memory, his ability to balance a checkbook, and his ability to walk. He would fall out of bed every night. We were finally left with a father, a grandfather, a human being, who could no longer function.

After he died at age 80 in 2000, I retreated into denial. I ignored the disease and mourned the man. When I decided to create a quilt for this exhibit I made a conscious effort to confront this disease. I spent hours sewing and thinking about Dad and how Alzheimer's robbed him of his dignity. This wonderful man, who was so good at taking care of his family, was reduced to sleeping in diapers. Dementia slowly stripped him of everyday functions that we all take for granted, like leaves falling from a tree, until nothing was left.

Alzheimer's disease is a disorder that destroys brain cells. It is the leading cause of dementia, a condition that involves gradual memory loss, decline in the ability to perform routine tasks, disorientation, difficulty in learning, loss of language skills, impairment of judgment, and personality changes. As the disease progresses, people with Alzheimer's become unable to care for themselves. The loss of brain cells eventually leads to the failure of other systems in the body.

Confusion

30" x 32½"
Elsie Campbell
Dodge City, Kansas

Elsie is an award-winning quiltmaker, international teacher, writer, and editor. She is the author of *Nine Patch and Snowball Quilts* and *Winning Stitches*. Her 75 plus awards include Best of Show—Quilt America! 2000, Mary Krickbaum Award for Best Hand Quilting—National Quilt Association, 2001, and Excellence in Hand Workmanship Award—American Quilter's Society's 2003.

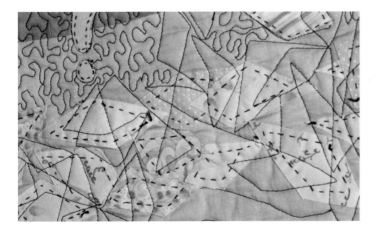

Alzheimer's is confusion. Commonplace things become mysterious, their identity and purpose impossible to discern. With confusion often comes loneliness and isolation.

The Lone Star parallels the progression of Alzheimer's. In the early stage (top), only one or two pieces are confused. A question mark and its mirrored image form a heart. As the disease progresses (middle), pieces are mixed up, left out, and transposed. Things don't quite make sense anymore. Patches become misshapen and distorted.

In the final stages (bottom), even the central purple diamonds, one's deepest memories, become distorted and go missing. Finally, memories fade and become nearly unrecognizable. Patches appear to lie in a pile on a table.

Generally the progression of Alzheimer's disease is characterized this way:

Mild or early-stage: decreased knowledge of recent occasions or current events, impaired ability to perform challenging mental arithmetic (counting backwards from 100 by 7s), reduced memory of personal history, and behavioral changes.

Moderate or mid-stage: major gaps in memory (current address, telephone number), needs assistance with day-to-day activities are essential. As this stage progresses patients may lose awareness of their surroundings, occasionally forget the name of people close to them, and may experience delusions, hallucinations, or compulsive repetitive behaviors.

Severe or late-stage: loss of ability to respond to the environment, the ability to speak, and ultimately to control movement such as eating, walking, smiling, continence, and swallowing.

Confusion

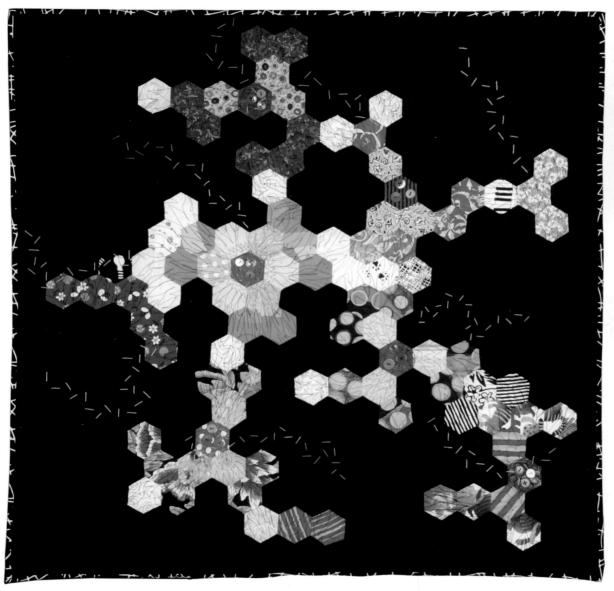

Gaps

30¾" x 30¾"
Cindy Cooksey
Irvine, California

Cindy is a native Southern California fiber artist whose works have been shown, among other places, at Quilt Visions 2002; Quilt Expos in Lyon, Innsbruck, Barcelona; International Quilt Festival in Houston; and La Jolla Fiber Arts Gallery. Her quilts typically employ appliqué, vivid colors, and a sense of humor.

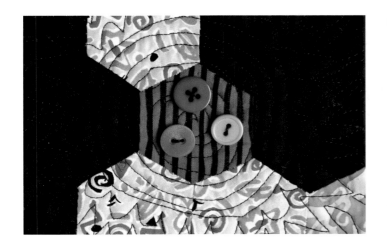

This is "Gaps." It refers to the gaps in memory that people with Alzheimer's disease experience. The gaps grow and spread until memories become unrecognizable, impossible to retrieve.

My grandmother had Alzheimer's. I remember her flower garden, so I used leftover hexagon patches from a Grandmother's Flower Garden quilt for this project.

I made this quilt because both of my grandmothers had Alzheimer's, as did my father, as does my mother, as does her sister. Finding a cure is obviously a very important priority for me and my siblings, and that's why I am supporting the Alzheimer's Art Quilt Initiative in this way.

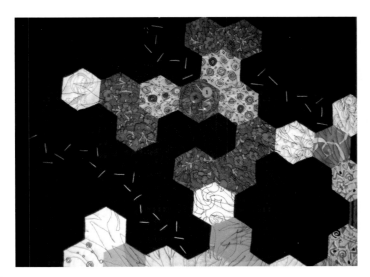

The greatest known risk factor is increasing age, and most individuals with the illness are 65 and older. The likelihood of developing Alzheimer's approximately doubles every five years after age 65. After age 85, the risk reaches nearly 50%.

Another risk factor is family history. Research has shown that those who have a parent or sibling with Alzheimer's are two to three times more likely to develop the disease than those who do not.

Scientists have so far identified one gene that increases risk of Alzheimer's but does not guarantee an individual will develop the disorder. Research has also revealed certain rare genes that virtually guarantee an individual will develop Alzheimer's. The genes that directly cause the disease have been found in only a few hundred extended families worldwide and are thought to account for a tiny percentage of cases. Experts believe the vast majority of cases are caused by a complex combination of genetic and non-genetic influences.

Trying To Remember

34" x 30"
Linda Dunn
Cambridge, Massachusetts

After graduating from Kirkland College, **Linda** worked her way up the food chain in the publishing and high tech worlds. Then she kicked it all away for art school. Now shocked to be past 50, she lives with her husband, raises her daughter, works at her art, and passionately loves all three.

My father watched his five siblings descend into dementia before him. He lived in fear and, at 70, ruefully celebrated that he'd had a handful more good years than any other person in his family.

By the time I brought him my first child, though, my father was slipping. He got lost coming home from the supermarket. He asked, "What day is it?" every few hours. A photographer since childhood, he couldn't get the film out of his camera. A new grandfather, he couldn't remember my baby's name or sex.

I thought it was the hardest week of my life. But each visit after that was harder.

This quilt has been brewing in my heart since my father died, at 84. Mercifully ill of pneumonia, he still recognized his wife and daughters, though we were all frozen years younger in his mind.

I hand dyed the fabrics in this quilt, then over printed them with words and images. Edges are deliberately blurred. Meaning hovers just out of focus. The eye travels around the surface, but even the resting points refuse to give up their message.

I remember my father trying to remember what he knew he used to know. I tried to weave that anguish into beauty here. I love this quilt, but I find it hard to look at. "Mom," said my daughter, now twelve, "It's supposed to be hard to look at. It's about hard things."

Scientists have so far identified one Alzheimer's risk gene called apoliprotein E-e4 (APOE-e4). Everyone inherits a copy of some form of APOE from each parent. Those who inherit one copy of APOE-e4 have an increased risk of developing Alzheimer's. Those who inherit two copies have an even higher risk, but not a certainty. Scientists do not yet know how APOE-e4 raises risk.

Trying To Remember

Sundown

33" x 45"
Beth Hartford
Zion, Illinois

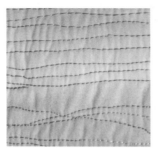

Beth began quilting in 1984. She learned to hand dye fabric using Procion dyes in 1998 and fell in love with that creative process. She began using her exquisite hand-dyed and hand-painted fabrics almost exclusively in her own quilts, and now produces this fabric for other quilters and textile artists through her company, Quilters Stitch Together.

When I first heard the term "sundowning," referring to the agitated behavior some Alzheimer's patients exhibit after the sun sets, I thought of all the beautiful sunsets I've enjoyed. My father is largely responsible for my appreciation of nature and its beauty. Together, we have taken countless photographs of sunsets.

This quilt is of my father, enjoying the view from the window where he spends the majority of his time sitting in his recliner. I see him in silhouette because so much of his personality and vitality has been lost to Alzheimer's. He is a shadow of himself.

Even this view, one he sees every day, has become unfamiliar to him at times. He is often unsure of where he is and who he is with. It frightens him. And, it breaks my heart to see him deny that my mother is his wife of more than 50 years, or claim that one of his children is unknown to him.

I made this quilt as a tribute to my dad, to his life, and to his family. It represents his final years... hopefully he can live out the rest of his life peacefully, enjoying the beauty of the sunset.

Studies indicate that as many as 20 percent of persons with Alzheimer's will, at some point, experience periods of increased confusion, anxiety, agitation and disorientation beginning at dusk and continuing throughout the night. While experts are not certain how or why these behaviors occur, many attribute them to late-day confusion, or "sundowning." This can be caused by end-of-day exhaustion, an upset in the "internal body clock" causing a biological mix-up between day and night, disorientation due to the inability to separate dreams from reality, or less need for sleep which is common among older adults.

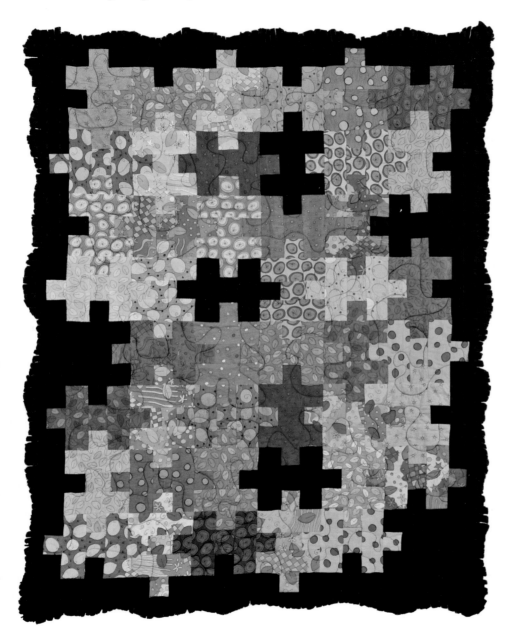

Puzzling Memories

36" x 46"
Peggy Mages
Lake View, New York

In her "former life," **Peggy** was a children's librarian who amassed a fantastic personal library of quilting books, but had little time to open them. Now retired, she is finding plenty of opportunity to put her collection to use and attempt those projects she had previously only imagined. Making charity and gift quilts provide her greatest satisfaction.

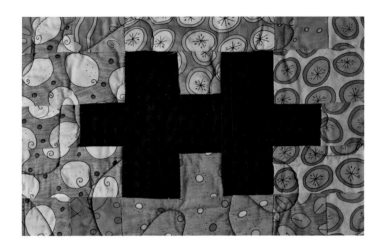

The pieces in this jigsaw puzzle represent individual experiences that make up our memories. When this project began, all the fabric pieces were bright, bold, and easily distinguished, one from another. So it is before the onset of Alzheimer's.

Things slowly began to change. The fabrics were dyed different shades of brown. Colors, as memories do, began to fade. Some vanished completely leaving only blank, black spaces.

As the process continued, even the well-defined rectangular shape of the quilt became distorted. The border is now uneven, unraveled, and ragged as if it were coming apart. Meandering, black quilting stitches seem to have no beginning or end. The ravages of Alzheimer's disease are unstoppable and irreversible.

Special thanks to Liz Schwartz and Stephen Seifert for allowing me to use their "Quilter's Puzzle" pattern for this quilt. It is available at eQuiltPatterns.com.

Alzheimer's disease is a fatal disease. It is not a normal part of aging. It is a devastating disorder of the brain's nerve cells that impairs memory, thinking, and behavior and leads, ultimately, to death. If the individual has no other serious illness, the loss of brain function itself will cause death.

At this time, there is no medical treatment to cure or stop the progression of Alzheimer's disease.

Puzzling Memories

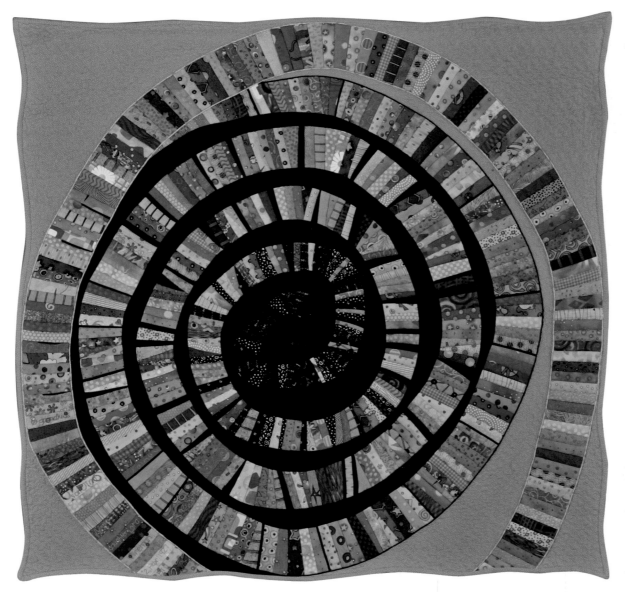

Out Of Control: In Memory Of Bill

36½" x 36¼"
Kate Laucomer
Lincoln, Nebraska

Kate made her first quilt (a scrappy one-patch) with her grandmother when she was 12. In 1993, she started her own pattern company, **Homespun Charm**, which caters to beginners and more experienced quilters who want quick projects with a primitive look. Kate's exhibit quilt demonstrates her versatility as she moves beyond traditional with a powerful visual statement.

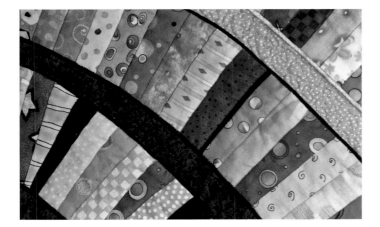

We met Bill and his wife Annie almost 20 years ago. They adopted our family and we adopted them. Bill was this big, kind, godly, gentle man. He was great with children. My kids adored him. My husband and I enjoyed his friendship.

Slowly, we noticed Bill was changing. He forgot things. Simple activities now confused him. He needed help to do the easiest things. Eventually, he was diagnosed with Alzheimer's.

We live in the country. Everything around us is green and growing—the quilt's background. Around us is every color imaginable: wildflowers, cows, thistle, tractor, deer, sunflowers, birds, weeds, horses, my kids outside playing, our silly little dog running in the yard. Bright, bold colors are everywhere.

Important names and dates are embroidered on the path. At first the Alzheimer's (black) is barely noticeable. But gradually it creeps in more and more separating Bill from the rest of us; he is now on a different path, moving towards a downward spiral.

Finally, only a bit of life's colors remain. At last, it's only black. The person you loved is no longer there. Bill passed away on April 8, 2006—the date embroidered at the center of the spiral.

More than 5 million Americans have Alzheimer's disease. The number of Americans with Alzheimer's has more than doubled since 1980.

Out Of Control: In Memory Of Bill

Once Upon A Time All The World Was Bright And Beautiful

**38" x 38"
Ronnie Doyal
Centerville, Ohio**

Ronnie is a native of the Southwest. Born in Texas and raised in New Mexico, her art often reflects those roots. She is a self-taught quilter but she considers herself a mother first and fits in quilting when there is time. In addition to quilting, she works part time as a photographer's assistant and takes lessons in Taekwondo where she has achieved the rank of 2nd Dan.

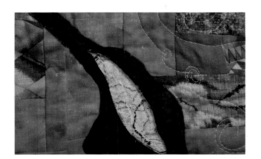

My grandmother (Granny) had Alzheimer's. Her name was Ela Bynum and though she lived to a ripe old age, this insidious disease plagued the last 15 years of her life.

It started out simple enough, so simple that her family hardly took notice; forgotten appointments, misplaced objects, not remembering how to play a favorite game of cards. Alzheimer's crept into our lives and wound its roots deep into the heart of the family: we didn't even know its name.

When Granny got to the point where she couldn't be left alone, my father and uncles hired a live-in companion. That lasted only a couple of months. The day Granny went wandering down the street with no clothes on, they put her in a nursing home.

In the home she was put in diapers and tied to a chair. I know in my head that it was to keep her from wandering away, but in my heart I can't quite get over that image of her.

But Granny adapted. The lady in the next bed became Bernice, her next-door neighbor. She thought my father was her husband, and my uncle her brother. She told me about riding motorcycles, something I am fairly certain she never did in her real life. She lived in her own little world while the rest of us mourned. The Granny I knew was gone forever.

A person with Alzheimer's disease will live an average of eight years and as many as 20 years or more from the onset of symptoms. From the time of diagnosis, people with Alzheimer's disease survive about half as long as those of similar age without dementia.

Once Upon A Time...

Unforgettable

30" x 60"
Tammie Bowser
South Pasadena, California

Tammie is the author and inventor of Quilted Photography, a system of creating incredibly realistic, pixilated images in fabric. She was taught to sew as a very young child and made her first garments at four years of age. Before starting her quilting career she spent 18 years as a professional fashion designer and patternmaker. Tammie's creativity enables her to design contemporary quilts, and contemporary quilting techniques without traditional rules or restrictions.

Unforgettable

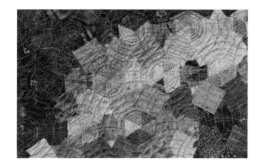

Alzheimer's took my grandmother's life. She lived with me a few years ago, and that is when I noticed changes in her. She had lots of fear and forgetfulness, she even got lost trying to drive home...in the same city she had been driving in for 40 years! I felt helpless and like she was slipping away from me. She was diagnosed with Alzheimer's later that year.

One of the first quilts I made using my mosaic quilt technique was this piece. I used an old black and white photograph of my grandmother. She studied ballet as a child. From a distance every detail seems to be visible. Yet, as one approaches, the details become a blur and disappear. It's like the beginnings of Alzheimer's. Unless you're around the person a lot, it's sometimes hard to tell something is wrong. From a distance all is well; up close, the image is a blur, as if parts are missing. It really hurt to watch her disappear, but I will never forget Faye Evalyn Taylor.

Some change in memory is normal as we grow older, but the symptoms of Alzheimer's disease are more than simple lapses in memory. People with Alzheimer's experience difficulties communicating, learning, thinking, and reasoning—problems severe enough to impact work, social activities and family life.

Ten Warning Signs of Alzheimer's

1. Memory loss	*6. Problems with abstract thinking*
2. Difficulty performing familiar tasks	*7. Misplacing things*
3. Problems with language	*8. Changes in mood or behavior*
4. Disorientation to time and place	*9. Changes in personality*
5. Poor or decreased judgment	*10. Loss of initiative*

Trying To Hold On

36" x 36"
Becky Goldsmith
Sherman, Texas

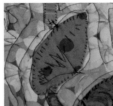

Becky is best known as half of the design team of *Piece O' Cake Designs*, whose patterns and cheerful color palette have charmed quilters since 1994. She is the co-author of 19 books and has taught nationally for more than 10 years. Becky's quilts, though often traditionally inspired, are always imaginative and fresh. Her workmanship is impeccable.

When I thought about what this quilt should be, I imagined myself. If I had Alzheimer's, would I stop quilting? I'm guessing that I would not—that I would continue to quilt, trying to hold onto this important part of who I am.

As the disease progressed, what would my quilt look like? Here, the workmanship shifts gradually, from very good in the center to pretty ragged at the edges. But you have to look closely to see the decline. Isn't that true of this disease as well? You can't always tell from the outside what's wrong, you have to look closely for signs.

When I look at this quilt, my eyes keep going back to the center. It is so crisp and pretty. If I were to get Alzheimer's I would hope that people remembered me not for who I was at the end, but who I was when I was still me.

Signals that form memories and thoughts move through an individual nerve cell as a tiny electrical charge.

Nerve cells connect to one another at synapses. When a charge reaches a synapse, it may trigger release of tiny bursts of chemicals called neurotransmitters.

The neurotransmitters travel across the synapse, carrying signals to other cells. Scientists have identified dozens of neurotransmitters.

Alzheimer's disease disrupts both the way electrical charges travel within cells and the activity of neurotransmitters.

Trying To Hold On

Fading Memories

38" x 31"
Linda Cooper
Burke, Virginia

Linda's family has endured her quilting obsession for 20 years. She credits many of her quilting abilities to her guild, Quilters Unlimited of Northern Virginia, and to the wonderful quilt teachers and workshops it has sponsored.

I tried to depict the fading reality that Alzheimer's brings. The flowers in the center and their surroundings are almost indistinguishable from one another. I painted the background with somber colors and brief splashes of brightness. The daylilies and free-cut stems are raw-edge machine appliquéd.

In the borders I've quilted sections of normal neurons with occasional damaged nerves with the beaded amyloid plaques, seen in the disease pathology.

The floral images are also in memory of my mother and grandmother who loved their gardens and loved growing beautiful flowers until Alzheimer's took away that ability.

Alzheimer's tissue has many fewer nerve cells and synapses than a healthy brain. Scientists are not absolutely sure what causes cell death and tissue loss in the Alzheimer brain, but plaques and tangles are prime suspects.

Plaques form when protein pieces called beta-amyloid (BAY-tuh AM-uh-loyd) clump together. Beta-amyloid comes from a larger protein found in the fatty membrane surrounding nerve cells. Beta-amyloid is chemically "sticky" and gradually builds up into plaques, which are abnormal clusters of protein fragments that build up between nerve cells.

The most damaging form of beta-amyloid may be groups of a few pieces rather than the plaques themselves. The small clumps may block cell-to-cell signaling at synapses. They may also activate immune system cells that trigger inflammation and devour disabled cells.

It's Like Grandpa's Memories Have Been Sucked Away

42" x 33½"
Barb Lamb
Baton Rouge, Louisiana

Barb Lamb is a domestic goddess (aren't all stay-at-home moms?), and mother of four. This is her first quilt in an exhibit. She has learned quilting from friends, books, and online quilt groups, while passionately gleaning tips and information anywhere she can. Barb says she will take a class, someday!

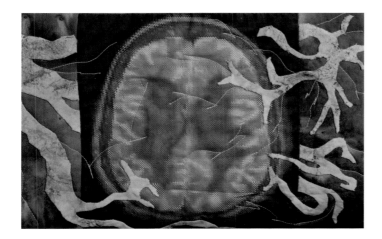

My grandfather, Joseph Heidecker, passed away when I was in the 6th grade. Still, his battle with Alzheimer's made a strong impression on me. Ever since that time I've had fears of my father getting it. Many times I look at my husband and children and fear the worst. What if someday I don't remember who they are? What if they are speaking to me and I have no memories of how they say I lived my life?

The sunset represents the end of my grandfather's days. The "black hole" in the sky sucks his memories into nothingness.

The gnarled old tree is now a skeleton of the wonderful tree that it once was, my grandfather. Manipulated photos of my grandfather, taken before he died, are dried leaves swirling in the wind. They are skewed and warped as the memories of Alzheimer's patients become…nonsensical.

Below is a cross-section of the earth. The roots are embracing, and tangled around the scan of an Alzheimer's brain. The disease now controls the life of the tree…or rather, controls the end of that life.

The fabric for this quilt was hand painted by Debbie Adcock.

Alzheimer's disease leads to nerve cell death and tissue loss throughout the brain. Over time, the brain shrinks dramatically, affecting nearly all its functions.

The cortex shrivels up, damaging areas involved in thinking, planning, and remembering. Shrinkage is especially severe in the hippocampus, an area of the cortex that plays a key role in formation of new memories.

It's Like Grandpa's Memories …

Holes In My Memory

34½" x 33½"
Donna Hudson
Seattle, Washington

Donna is a fabric artist in love with color and form. She started doing traditional quilts (after life as a database engineer) and discovered the joy of contemporary fabrics and original design. This is the first time her work is exhibited nationally.

Dedicated to Grandma Esther.

My thoughts—they're not as clear as they used to be. There are threads through a fog of gray. They lack precision. There are still some bright moments, but things are foggy and off-kilter. What really scares me are the holes.

This is what I think Alzheimer's is like. Grandma had it; Dad's scared of being diagnosed with it. So I've tried staying informed, reading up on symptoms and disease progression. I hope I'm not in line for it and that research makes significant progress as I age.

The quilt is predominantly low contrast to represent unclear thoughts. The couching threads were deliberately made to show tension. Tension "shows" in Alzheimer's families. The bright spots are good days. The tulle holes are fuzzy, empty places.

As the Alzheimer's brain shrinks due to widespread cell death, the ventricles (fluid-filled spaces within the brain) grow larger. Individuals lose a sense of where their body is in relation to the environment around them. They lose their ability to communicate, to recognize family and loved ones, and to care for themselves.

Holes In My Memory

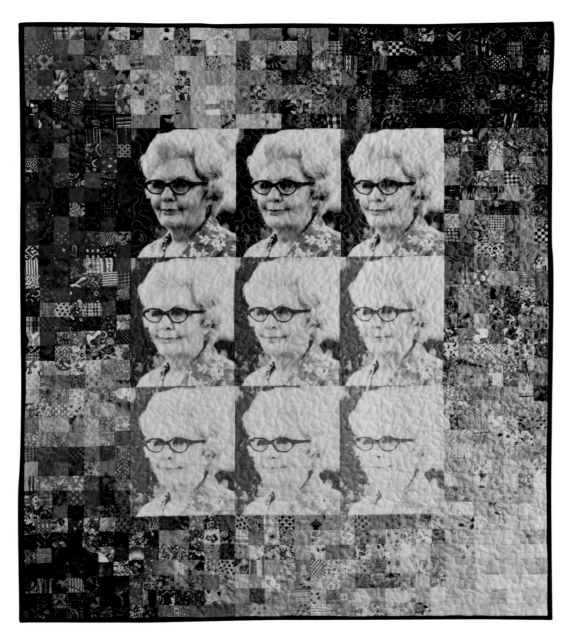

Nevilyn

35" x 41"
Linda J. Huff
Algonquin, Illinois

Linda has had her hands in fabric all of her life. She began constructing doll clothes and progressed through cross-stitch, crochet, garment construction, crewel embroidery, counted cross-stitch, and most recently, art quilts. Linda attempts to incorporate her diverse knowledge of sewing techniques in her work.

Nevilyn

Nevilyn was born June 14, 1915, and she is my grandmother. She learned to sew because as a child she had rheumatic fever and was never allowed to do anything strenuous. In January of 1936 she married Jerry and they started their family. Mostly they worked and lived their lives, struggling through the tough times and rejoicing in the good times.

When it was time to retire, Grandpa hooked up a travel trailer to his truck and told Grandma they were going to visit all of the places they had always wanted to see. If they did those things now, he insisted, when they got too old to travel at least they would have the memories of all that they had seen and done.

In 1999 Grandpa died. Then Grandma was diagnosed with Alzheimer's. The woman who sits in the nursing home today has no memories of friends or family or the special things that she and her husband did especially for this time in her life. Nevilyn was once lively and vibrant. In the end only a ghost of her former self remains.

There are 868 small squares in the border. They speak of so many things in my grandmother's life: the fabric that she worked with to make clothes and quilts, her attention to small details, her desire that things be done the "right" way, and her love of color. They also symbolize all of her memories, funny stories, sad times, the trips she took, and the things she has done. All the little pieces of her life are now lost to her forever.

By 2050, the number of individuals age 65 and over with Alzheimer's could range from 11 million to 16 million unless science finds a way to prevent or effectively treat the disease.

Losing My Mind A Piece At A Time

37½" x 58"
Jannett Caldwell
Avondale, Pennsylvania

Inspired by her artistic nature, **Jannett** has been creating quilts for her family and friends since 1971. She welcomes any child wanting to make a fabric creation into her studio. In addition to teaching children to love quilting, Jannett uses her quilts to help others. She makes quilts for the local rescue squad and for sick children. Another passion is finding, documenting, and re-creating old quilts. For the past two years she has assisted the Delaware Quilt Documentation Project. Alzheimer's has touched Jannett's family and, by extension, her art.

My quilt symbolizes my mother's coming battle with Alzheimer's. She realizes her mind is going, and she has a great sadness, shown by the weeping eyes.

The top two rows of the quilt are 30's reproduction fabrics, and the circles are feed sack fabric. These fabrics represent my mother's bright and happy childhood.

As the blocks continue downwards, blank patches show the memory loss, and finally the falling apart of the mind altogether.

An early diagnosis for people with dementia and their families has some advantages:

- *Time to make choices that maximize quality of life.*
- *Lessened anxieties about unknown problems.*
- *A better chance of benefiting from treatment.*
- *More time to plan for the future.*

It is also important for a physician to determine the cause of memory loss or other symptoms. Some dementia-like symptoms can be reversed if they are caused by treatable conditions, such as depression, drug interaction, thyroid problems, excess use of alcohol, or certain vitamin deficiencies.

Losing My Mind A Piece At A Time

Russian Olive Trees

30" x 40"
Debbie Bowles
Burnsville, Minnesota

Designs from **Debbie's** *Maple Island Quilts Company* are loved the world over, from Africa to Australia. You may have seen her on various quilting shows on TV, demonstrating her inventive curves or one of her slightly non-traditional designs. **Debbie's** style is "controlled inventive," achievable, and fun.

Russian Olive Trees

For many years when my mother-in-law, Martha Louise Bowles, an incredible gardener, visited us she would comment on a stand of Russian olive trees near our home. She would comment when we drove past them as we left the house and again when we returned, as if she had forgotten that she had already told us how much she enjoyed them. It was so predictable that we dismissed it as a quirk of aging. It would be quite a few years before we realized this was probably the first sign of dementia.

The units of the quilt signify perceptions of Alzheimer's and how it changes the lives of so many. The long black-and-white narrow curves in the center represent the path of life filled with ordinary curves and bumps.

The broken curves on the right represent the first symptoms of Alzheimer's, the repeating. The brighter stripes that travel in short spurts in many directions represent the fractured lives of Alzheimer's patients, their families, and friends.

Life continues in the border but in slightly less than bright white for all who stand near those with Alzheimer's.

In the early stages of Alzheimer's, friends, family, or co-workers begin to notice deficiencies. Problems with memory or concentration may be measurable in clinical testing or discernible during a detailed medical interview. Common difficulties include:

◄▢ *Reading a passage and retaining little material.*

◄▢ *Losing or misplacing a valuable object.*

◄▢ *Decline in ability to plan or organize.*

A Porsche Problem

37" x 36½"
Georgia Bonesteel
Flat Rock, North Carolina

Georgia was the creator and host of public television's *Lap Quilting* for 12 years, and the author of eight books plus the Spinning Spools pattern club. For almost 20 years she and her husband operated Bonesteel Hardware and Quilt Corner. Georgia served as President of the International Quilt Association, and received the IQA's 2001 Silver Star Salute and Bernina's 2002 Leadership Award. She was inducted into the Quilters Hall of Fame in 2003. Most recently she has co-produced *The Great American Quilt Revival*, a one-hour PBS television documentary that explores the historic roots of quilting as well as the people, the art, and the economics of the 20th century quilt world.

There once was a guy from Chicago
Who was quite fond of making his "cah go"
Just a smidgen too fast
So he's built up a past
And is wanted from Jax to Wells Fargo!

~Martha Graves

A Porsche Problem

The family situation was such that Earl did not understand that he could no longer drive safely. Yes, our father, Earl Jinkinson, did love his Porsches. He had a form of dementia and couldn't find his way home. We tried the driver license removal routine, but that did not work. We even had a policeman come and counsel him, telling him he could no longer drive in North Carolina. "Fine," he said, "South Carolina is just down the road."

The only solution was for Jill, my sister, to drive "it" away to Pennsylvania. Thereafter he related that he had two daughters; one who taught quilting all over the country, was on TV, wrote books, blah, blah, and another daughter who stole cars! His last car remains in the family and a constant reminder of his driving escapades.

Tips To Limit Driving

- *Ask a doctor to write the person a "do not drive" prescription.*
- *Disable the car by removing the distributor cap or battery.*
- *Control access to the car keys.*
- *Have the person tested by the Department of Motor Vehicles.*

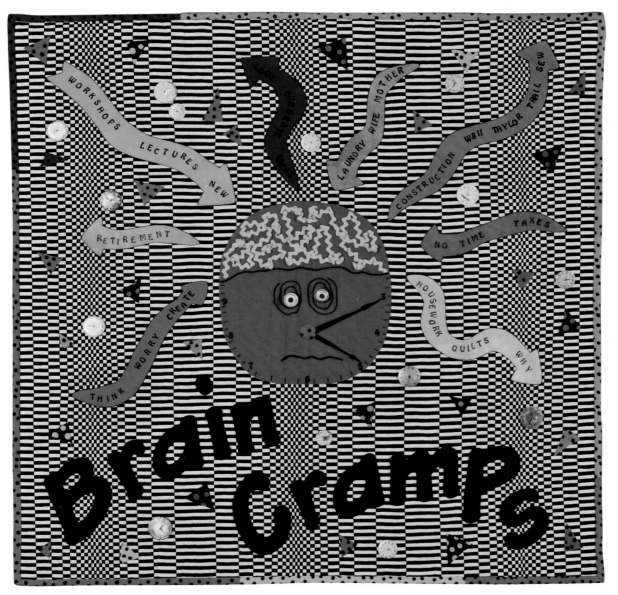

Brain Cramps

30" x 30"
Mary Stori
Clyde, North Carolina

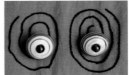

Mary enjoys using embellishments to enhance her quilt designs. She has written six books and recently completed an instructional beading DVD. A sought-after teacher on the national circuit, Mary was named 2004 Teacher of the Year by *The Professional Quilter.*

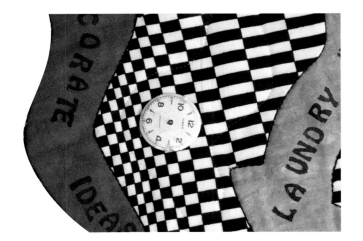

Having a parent with Alzheimer's makes you hyper-sensitive to everyday forgetfulness, the kind that comes from the busy stressed-out kind of life we all lead. You wonder every time you forget where you put your keys, or overlook one little detail among the hundreds of things you juggle every day, that it's a sign that you're going to get it too. Every little glitch in the system, every brain cramp, can be a cause for worry. So you stress some more…and forget something else!

Brain cramps are not the cause of lost memories, the forgotten meaning of all things that used to be familiar, or the disrupted flow of fluid thinking—Alzheimer's is! My mom is in the late stage of Alzheimer's. She complains constantly (and I mean constantly) and has for the last three years that her head aches. I believe now, and have all along (and finally so does her doctor), that she's not really experiencing a "headache." Rather she uses this term to describe her confusion and inability to think clearly, not unlike what non-stop brain cramps might feel like.

The stresses that cause my brain cramps are on this quilt. There are old watch faces beaded onto the background; I'm always up against the clock. They also stand for the true tragedy of Alzheimer's—time and memory lost, stolen from a productive vibrant life. It is something we all fear.

People with Alzheimer's disease often forget simple words or substitute unusual words, making their speech or writing hard to understand. They may be unable to find their toothbrush, for example, and instead ask for "that thing for my mouth."

Brain Cramps

Mixed Emotions

30" x 35"
Meena Schaldenbrand
Plymouth, Michigan

An enthusiastic quilter of 25 years, **Meena** has made well over 200 quilts. Many are reactions to personal history or current events. She has exhibited throughout the United States, and overseas, including the US embassy residence in Islamabad, Pakistan. Her current work includes the use of metal embellishments, including aluminum, brass, copper, hardware cloth, gutter guard, window screen, and pop cans.

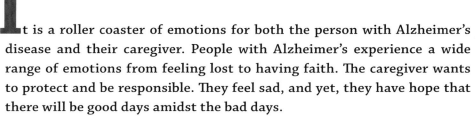

It is a roller coaster of emotions for both the person with Alzheimer's disease and their caregiver. People with Alzheimer's experience a wide range of emotions from feeling lost to having faith. The caregiver wants to protect and be responsible. They feel sad, and yet, they have hope that there will be good days amidst the bad days.

The memory tree has falling leaves. The helping hand is for support, because love never ends.

Receiving a diagnosis of Alzheimer's unleashes a wide range of emotions:

- *Denial about having dementia.*
- *Fear of losing people important to you.*
- *Loneliness because no one seems to understand what you are going through.*
- *Frustration with not making yourself understood.*
- *Loss of the way you used to see yourself.*
- *Depression or anger about the way your life is changing.*

Caring for someone who has Alzheimer's disease can be overwhelming, exhausting, and stressful. A family caregiver may feel loss over changes in relationships with a loved one with Alzheimer's, other family members and friends.

Alzheimer's caregivers report that they frequently experience high levels of stress. Too much stress can be damaging to both a caregiver and the person with Alzheimer's.

Mixed Emotions

Faded Memory

30" x 50"
Christine Adams
Rockville, Maryland

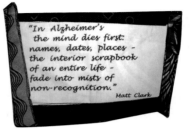

"In Alzheimer's the mind dies first: names, dates, places – the interior scrapbook of an entire life – fade into mists of non-recognition."
Matt Clark

Using beads, buttons, photo imaging, and other embellishment, **Christine's** quilts tell stories. Her work is in the collections of Kaiser Permanente, The Children's Inn, The Greater Hospital of Baltimore, G Street Fabrics, and more. Her eclectic background includes studio artist; director of Rockville Arts Place; financial management for nonprofits; teaching art, English, and mathematics; and holistic healing.

My Dad lived with me from the onset of his dementia until his death. My sister and I, along with our families, shared the responsibility of caring for him. Life with Dad was often frustrating but also poignant and memorable.

Once when I was out Dad decided that he was going to run away. My inventive children came up with a great way to keep Dad safe and at home. They agreed that yes he could leave and they would help. In case he got hungry though perhaps packing a lunch should be the first step. By the time food choices were made, taste-tested, and wrapped, Dad forgot his original purpose and I came home to a lively group snacking in the kitchen.

While Dad was in day care they visited the planetarium. Dad correctly identified the constellations and told stories of the stars. He was very entertaining. The guide claimed Dad knew more about the stars than he did. While my father didn't remember the particulars of the occasion the pride and good humor lingered on.

I used raw-edge free motion quilting to assemble the quilt suggesting the raw and frayed emotions in Alzheimer's. Photo imagery is scattered throughout the quilt and the silk textiles (leftover neckties from another project) are fragmented representing the scattered and fragmented aspects of the minds of those with the disease.

No two people experience Alzheimer's disease in the same way. As a result, there is no one approach to care giving. Creative coping skills can make sure your loved one feels supported and leads a full life while it helps you preserve your own well-being.

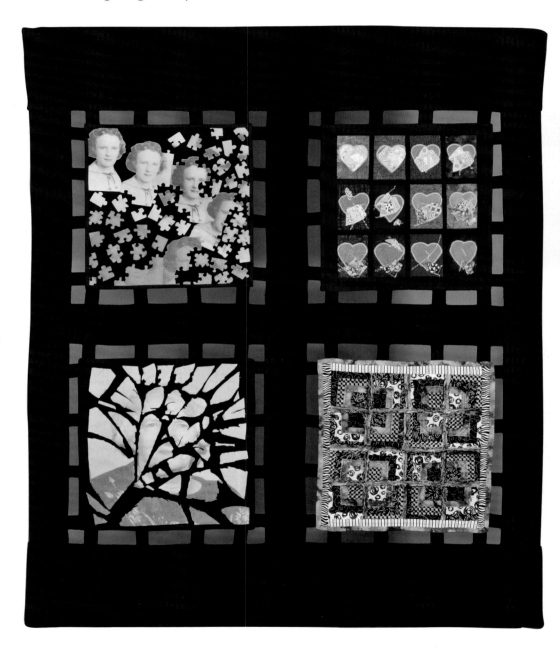

Shattered Lives

33" x 39"
Timi Bronson
Salem, Connecticut

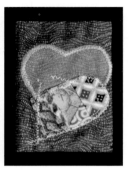

Timi lives in a small town in Connecticut with her husband. She is the primary caregiver for her parents who also live with them. She is the youngest of the four McCready sisters who each made a component of their exhibit quilt. Timi is an avid collector of fabric and finds some time every day to fondle her collection.

Cherile loves quilts. She has collected, reconstructed, and repaired antique quilts for more than twenty-five years, finding satisfaction in hand quilting these. After participating in a round robin with her three sisters, she found a whole new world of quilting and now even machine quilts!

Sandra is the second of the four McCready sisters. She lives in Sun City Center, Florida, with her husband. She has been sewing as long as she can remember and started quilting after receiving a maple leaf quilt wall hanging from her elder sister more than 20 years ago. She especially enjoys making miniature quilts.

First of the sisters, *Dona* has sewn since age 10, at one time designing and sewing for others. Along the way she discovered that, unlike sewing, quilting only required a small amount of many fabrics. Quilting (at least collecting fabrics) became an addiction. At Timi's instigation, Dona now enjoys the challenge of making art quilts.

My three sisters and I each created a complete 12" x 12" quilt. I combined the four quilts into the finished piece you see here.

Each of us, and our families, has been affected by this horrible disease and how it affects our mother. It has truly shattered our lives. This quilt represents that shattering. The black header, footer, bars, and spacers represent the black voids that are left in our lives when Mom isn't with us; it's the place that Mom goes during those times. The spaces between the bars represent the missing pieces from her life and ours.

Row 1, Quilt 1: Dona McCready-Lewis, Tupper Lake, New York

Row 1, Quilt 2: Sandra McCready-Bianco, Sun City Center, Florida

Row 2, Quilt 1: Timi Bronson, Salem, Connecticut

Row 2, Quilt 2: Cherile Johnston, Macks Creek, Missouri

If you are a caregiver, you can expect to have feelings of loss and grief as your life and the person you love are changed by Alzheimer's disease. These feelings are difficult, but they are normal.

- *Accept and acknowledge your feelings.*
- *Share feelings with family and friends.*
- *Talk with a professional who specializes in grief counseling.*
- *Attend a support group where you can talk with other caregivers.*
- *Do things you enjoy.*
- *Try to feel comfortable accepting and celebrating good things in your life.*
- *Find ways to forgive yourself.*

Shattered Lives

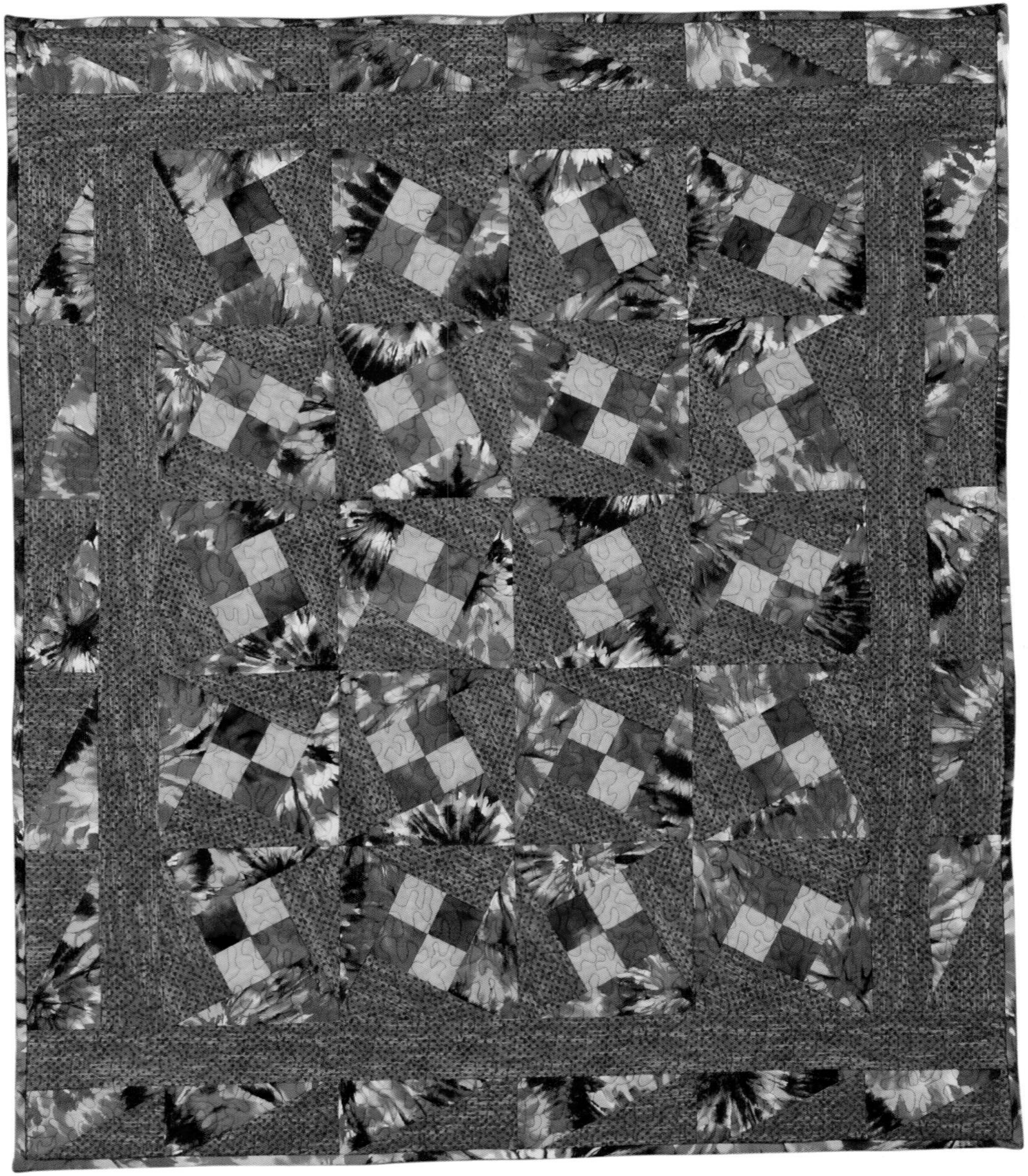

Shards Of Memory

33" x 39"
Judith Szumlas
Maquoketa, Iowa

Judith is a retired surgical nurse. She and her sister take care of their 92-year-old mother who has Alzheimer's disease and cannot be left alone. Quilting has become the perfect pastime, allowing Judith to keep an eye on Mom while she nurtures her own creative spirit. Judith has made only a few quilts so far, but has visions of dozens more dancing through her head.

I am a novice quilter with only four quilts under my belt. My interest in quilting started because my sister and I share the care of our 92-year-old mother who has moderate Alzheimer's disease.

The old saying "out of sight, out of mind" is most appropriate for Mom. If you are not in her direct vision, she thinks she is alone and will yell for you or wander the house looking for you. So, for her sake, and my sanity, I began sewing in our family room to remain close to her during the day.

Quilting has now opened a new world for me and is a way to relax and use my creativity. I pray daily for a cure for this destructive disease that steals away one's memory, and I hope that these quilts will provide an increase in awareness, encouragement, and research. This is why I decided to share my quilt and my story with you.

Thank you to Marcia Hohn, who graciously gave me permission to use her pattern for my quilt.

Shards Of Memory

Make the best of a difficult situation by allowing your caregiving activities to include healthy activities for you. Learning new skills and nurturing your own creativity are good for your mental health.

Women Who Were

38" x 43½"
by Sonia M. Callahan
Piedmont, California

Sonia, a mother of four, has lived and worked in many different places, including Australia, Indonesia, and England. She credits traveling for her love of ethnic fabrics, which she uses in most of her quilts. Her quilts have appeared in several publications, and an article she authored on cyanotype was published in *The American Quilter.* Her interest in quilting began when she helped immigrant students use their needle skills to subsidize their incomes. She is a most versatile teacher, having taught pre-school to community college and everything in between.

My quilt captures a moment in the life of an Alzheimer's patient. The poem illustrates the sad reality of fluctuation between connect and disconnect periods that are so common to this illness. I created this quilt in honor of my mother, Mary Melichar, who would be so pleased to know that she is helping others.

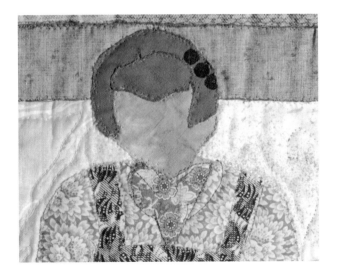

Who are these women sitting here?
Do I know you?
Are you the one who taught the kids?
Are you the one I saw at the bank?
Did you stand there when my babes were born?
I do not know. I do not know about many things.
This I know… I am not who I was before.
I am here.
Like the window view, I am hazy,
Not a part of that world out there.
My world is here.
I sit, I nap, I dream.
Time is meals, medicine and bed.
My days are planned.
I am with others, they sit near me.
Yet, I am alone, they know not who I am.
These are my days.
One day and then the next.
I am here.
This is my world.

Women Who Were

Nearly half of all nursing home residents have Alzheimer's disease or other dementias.

I Like The Red

30" x 38"
Morna McEver Golletz
Laytonsville, Maryland

Morna is the editor and publisher of *The Professional Quilter*, a business journal for serious quilters. She has had a needle in her hands since the age of three when she threaded needles for her great-great-grandmothers. She discovered quilting in 1977 and hasn't looked back since. She has won awards in both her fields of creative endeavor: quilting and journalism.

My mother has always had a wonderful sense of color. She earned a degree in Interior Design and went on to teach and win awards for her watercolor paintings. She developed early onset Alzheimer's disease in her early 60's. As the disease progressed, she lost the ability to draw, finally scribbling with a pencil, using the wrong end. She also lost the sense to distinguish color, except for red.

My sisters and I would take her out, and, while she might be stimulated by new surroundings, we frequently heard, "I like the red." At a quilt show surrounded by wonderful pieces, she would say, "I like the red," only for me to discover she meant the azaleas used as floor decoration.

Today she lives in an Alzheimer's home near three of her five daughters, her sister, and her 99-year-old mother. She barely speaks, has difficulty walking, and can't feed herself. I don't know if she sees the red any longer.

I wanted to depict her loss by breaking down the North Carolina Lily block into segments, gradually taking more and more color away. I'm sure if my mom could express herself, she would say, "I like the red."

Early onset Alzheimer's disease is a rare form of Alzheimer's in which individuals are diagnosed before the age of 65. Less than 10 percent of all Alzheimer's patients have early onset. Early onset Alzheimer's is associated with mutations in genes located on chromosomes 1, 14, and 21.

I Like The Red

Remember When?

36" x 36"
Barbara Campbell
Pine Brook, New Jersey

Barbara is a quilt and pattern designer who also has a background in technical reading for magazine publications as well as individual designers. She was editor of two quilting magazines and has written and contributed to several books, including *A Gathering of Days* by Elisa Wilson. She is the author of *Denim Divas* (with Jacqui Clarkson) and *Holiday Quilts* (with Yolanda Fundora). Barbara and Yolanda also design fabric for the quilting industry.

My mom was one of my biggest fans. She still recognizes me, but it really doesn't register. She doesn't know who I have become and what I do any more.

It took a long time for me to decide what I wanted to be when I grew up. (I began my quilting career at the ripe old age of 53.) I miss talking about, and sharing, my successes with my mother. Since my dad is gone, she is the only family member left to share with and it saddens me that she is so clueless.

When I saw this fabric I thought, "Remember when we used to communicate?" The envelopes and stamps, which would have been used in my mom's younger days, made me realize how much I miss talking with her, sharing my life with her. It pains me to see her slowly disappearing. I miss her.

Since my mother took the same path as her mother, I am very concerned about what lies in my future. I am anxious to do as much as I can now, within an industry that I love, to make the future a brighter one—before I forget what it is I want to do!

This quilt is in tribute to my mother, Betty Lyons, who is suffering from Alzheimer's.

It's normal to feel loss when you care about someone who has Alzheimer's disease. Alzheimer's gradually takes away the person you know and love.

Remember When?

Underlying Current

33½" x 33½"
Ami Simms
Flint, Michigan

First introduced to quilt making in 1975 while conducting anthropological research among the Old Order Amish, **Ami** began a teaching career eight years later. She has taught throughout the US and in seven foreign countries, and was named Teacher of the Year in 2005 by *The Professional Quilter*. She is the author of eight books, numerous patterns, and is the creator/curator of the *Worst Quilt In The World Contest*®. One of Ami's quilts was displayed in the US Ambassador's residence in Dakar, Senegal through the Arts in Embassies program. Through a quirk of fate, her participation in that program earned her an invitation to the White House. Ami writes a free monthly e-newsletter for over 18,000 quilters. She is the founder of *The Alzheimer's Art Quilt Initiative* and the curator of *Alzheimer's: Forgetting Piece by Piece*.

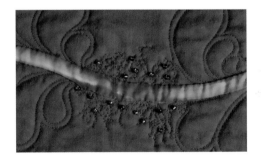

At breakfast one morning Mom stuck out her hand to introduce herself to my husband of 28 years:

"Hi, I'm Bee."

Underlying Current

Mom and I have always been super close. After Dad died, the plan was to have Mom move in with us when she got tired of living alone. Alzheimer's forced the issue in the fall of 2001.

My husband, Steve, and I took care of Mom for nearly 4½ years. On January 20, 2006 I moved her into an Alzheimer's facility because we could no longer keep her safe. It was the most difficult decision I've ever made. I was supposed to take care of her until the end.

Each decline in Mom's abilities meant taking over another small task. It was like another grain of sand, no big deal, so easy to do for someone you love so much. Only after she moved did I realize how much energy her care had taken, and how much of our lives it had consumed. Being "on duty" 24/7 felt like I was surrounded by a constant, underlying current.

The quilt's background is the anecdotal record of her loss, top to bottom, from the first signs, to her move to the Alzheimer's unit. The house, symbol of our love and family, is covered, literally, with the stresses of caregiving. Our dialogue (hers around the door, mine around the windows) is direct-printed on the sides of the house. Drug interactions on the roof represent my role as medical advocate. My darkest fears are printed around the heart—that I too will get this vile disease.

People with Alzheimer's change, and so do their needs. They often require care beyond what you can provide on your own. Look into in-home caregiver services and residential care.

Dear Diary

33" x 41"
Kathy Kansier
Ozark, Missouri

> Today the doctor said Mama has Alzheimer's. He said there is no cure for this and she will only get worse.

Kathy is a national quilting teacher, show judge, and AQS Certified Appraiser. She is the author of *Ozark Varieties*. As a quilt maker, she specializes in edge treatments, hand and machine appliqué, and crazy quilts. Kathy and her husband are building a quilters' retreat center on their property.

Dear Diary

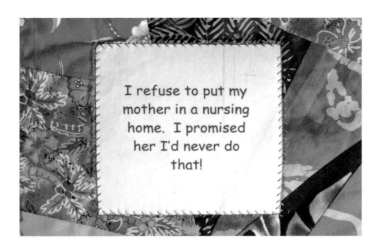

> I refuse to put my mother in a nursing home. I promised her I'd never do that!

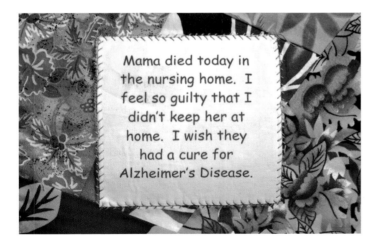

> Mama died today in the nursing home. I feel so guilty that I didn't keep her at home. I wish they had a cure for Alzheimer's Disease.

As a child I wrote daily thoughts in a pink diary, always signing it "Love Kathy." My quilt was written as though I was writing in my diary again. It chronicles the emotional struggles I had with my mother after she developed Alzheimer's. She was living with us at the time, and she was often argumentative. As I wrote the entries for the quilt blocks, I longed for my childhood days when Mama was normal. This was a difficult quilt for me to make.

I had always promised Mama that I would never put her in a nursing home. Our struggles finally reached that point where I had to break that promise. The strain of trying to take care of her was just too hard on my family and me. I knew of no programs that could help keep Mama at home, or to counsel us through our struggles. I would visit her at the nursing home often and she would always ask when she could live with us again. Each time she asked this it broke my heart. I felt like a terrible, selfish daughter with no patience or understanding. It was overwhelming at times and I often cried.

Mama died in her sleep during her afternoon nap. She looked so peaceful in death, but I still struggle with the fact that she died in a nursing home, that I hadn't kept her at home with us, and that she had Alzheimer's. I will always miss her.

Guilt can be a prevalent feeling for caregivers.

- _Thinking you could have done something differently._
- _Being able to enjoy life while your loved one may not._
- _Feelings that you have failed, especially if your loved one has been placed in a nursing home._

Mimi Has Squirrels In Her Attic

36" x 52"
Sue Lemmo
Clearfield, Pennsylvania

Sue is a high school art teacher currently working on three series of quilts: one reflecting her political and social involvement in work that often features dry humor; the second utilizing layers of sheer fabrics to create movement, texture, and pattern; and the third using a minimalist visual vocabulary to convey a sense of meditative reflection.

My quilt comes from an experience my grandmother had in the hospital. Her roommate told visitors that the squirrels under her bed were keeping her up at night. When my grandmother's doctor checked up on her each evening, he'd tell the squirrels to keep it down so her roommate could sleep.

My grandmother and her sisters loved to laugh. They had seen enough sorrow in life to know that they had better take joy where they found it. Even late in her life Grandma used to tell us to keep those squirrels under the bed quiet at night or she would have to come in and give them a talking to.

My great uncle passed away from complications due to Alzheimer's. My grandmother's baby sister cared for him for close to ten years until the night she called an ambulance because she was in excruciating pain. She told the EMT she had a lump in her breast, and when he asked her how long it had been there she replied, "Ten years."

Alzheimer's takes away more than memories of the patient; it often takes the health of the caregiver. This disease is not funny, but I learned from my grandmother and her sisters that if we don't laugh we might cry and you have to live life while you have it. I think she would have liked this crazy quilt.

Be A Healthy Caregiver

Get Help. You are not failing as a caregiver by asking others for assistance. Seek the support of family, friends, and community resources. Support group meetings are a good source of comfort and reassurance.

Take care of yourself. Watch your diet, exercise and get plenty of rest. Make time for shopping, lunch with friends, or even a golf outing. Take advantage of community services, such as adult day care or in-home companion services to care for your loved one while you take a break.

Mimi Has Squirrels In Her Attic

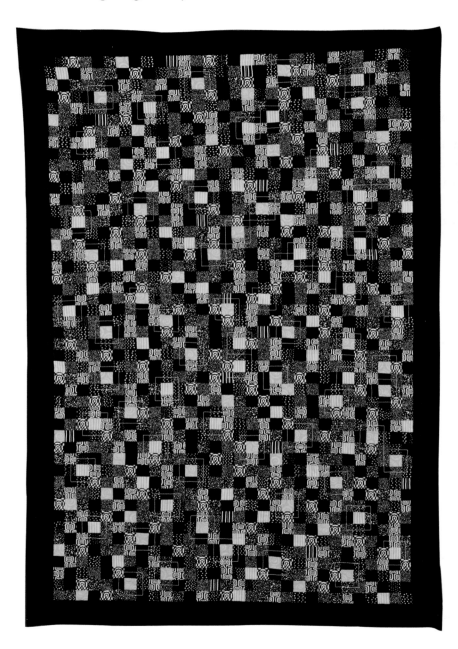

Lost Moments

32" x 48"
Naomi Adams
Leander, Texas

Naomi is a violence prevention educator and crisis center advocate by day, and an art quilter and wine enthusiast by night. She uses her background in interior design as her guide. Naomi lives in the hill country of Texas, with her husband, dog, and cats.

Lost Moments

I was a caregiver for a client with Alzheimer's. Often I was unsure of the best way to help him. Together, we were lost. I would say: "Let's try this today and see how it goes. We'll take it one day at a time." It was exhausting for us to get through a day, much less to face tomorrow.

Caregiving was very repetitive and often tedious, doing the same tasks over and over. My client's lime green Special Olympics T-shirt provided familiarity and comfort in a sea of uncertainty. The only way he would change into clean clothes was to offer him another clean lime green Special Olympics T-shirt.

There are 1,440 pieces in my quilt, one for each of the 1,440 minutes in a day. They represent the repetition of his care. The background fabrics create a sea of darkness that is as fatiguing to look at as it is to find meaning. Scattered lime green patches are for the T-shirts that gave him moments of comfort and solace, and gave me hope that perhaps tomorrow he would have more moments of clarity and peace.

It was a pleasure to serve this client. This quilt is dedicated to him and to all the caregivers who work tirelessly, often with no respite.

Understanding the point of view of the person with Alzheimer's is critical to providing appropriate care. Read Alzheimer's From The Inside Out *by Richard Taylor for a rare and poignant perspective. Another excellent book for caregivers is* Learning To Speak Alzheimer's *by Joanne Koenig Coste.*

Broken Memories

35" x 35"
Alice McGunigle
Shippenville, Pennsylvania

Alice has a lifelong interest in fabrics and quilting. She spent many years overseas, becoming familiar with fabric arts in Japan, China, and Southern Africa. Her quilts have appeared frequently in national shows and in several publications. A licensed commercial pilot, she has a degree in mathematics, and loves dogs and books.

Broken Memories

Alzheimer's patients lose memories, even of those closest to them. This quilt was made in memory of my mother-in-law, Teletha Harp McGunigle, who suffered from this dreadful disease. Among her last words to my husband were: "I know that you are important to me. Who are you?"

I scanned in the only old family photo that my husband has of his mother and their family. He is the little boy in the picture. Then I fractured and manipulated the images to symbolize the deterioration of the Alzheimer's mind. The quilting reinforces this theme, going from a light, happy, bubbly design to a dark, jagged, erratic style. The colors and the block design also start out as clear and upbeat, only to end in darkness and confusion.

One of the most heartwrenching experiences for the family of an Alzheimer's patient is literally watching the memories disappear. Alzheimer's disease can erase memories, change one's personality and behavior, and block the ability to communicate. Over time, the deepest and most profound memories of one's life are erased, leaving bewilderment and confusion.

Tears Of...

36" x 47"
Liz Kettle
Monument, Colorado

While **Liz** is new to the world of art quilts, she has been a traditional quilter for 18 years and a fabric connoisseur for more than 40 years. Liz lives in a world of happy chaos with three teenage boys, two cats, and one husband. She home schools two of her sons, works part time, and quilts in her spare time. Liz is as crazy about words as she is about fabric and is working on a book to combine the two passions of her life.

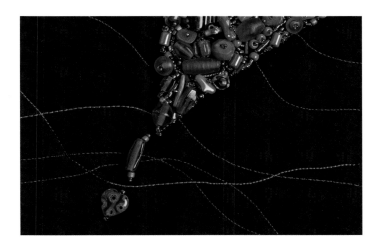

Tears of love, devotion, anger and frustration, how many tears does a caregiver shed? What inner strength supports them as they watch their loved ones disappear day by day? My great uncle cared for my great aunt as she retreated further and further from the world, from him, and from all that she loved.

Who takes care of the caregiver? Who gives back the life blood that is drained by their daily battles? Who fills their hearts back up again? Or are they just drained and empty after their war?

The red beads draining from the heart in my quilt represent the souls of the caregivers. Above the beads are crossed stitches. They cover the wounds, the hurts, and the sorrows suffered daily. Wavy lines, crossing and meandering, recall similar paths that memories take as they travel in our brains. Some of the lines are stitched in a variegated thread that goes to black and disappears, representing the loss of memory and hope.

I miss my great aunt; she was lost to us too soon. For many years I have been considering a quilt to honor her. She taught me how to sew. This quilt honors those who loved her. She would have liked that.

Direct and indirect costs of Alzheimer's and other dementia amount to more than $148 billion annually. This includes Medicare and Medicaid costs and the indirect cost to business of employees who are caregivers of persons with Alzheimer's.

Tears Of...

Shattered Memories, Shattered Lives

33½" x 42"
Ann Louise Mullard-Pugh
Las Vegas, Nevada

Ann creates her art surrounded by more fabric than the inventory of most quilt shops. Her most productive studio time is late at night when quilt stores are not open. Ann has been a successful business owner, wife, mother, and caregiver for her mother. Her work has traveled in *I Remember Mama I and II, America From the Heart,* and numerous other exhibits.

Alzheimer's affects those with the disease and the families who care for them and love them. This quilt represents a whole that is now shattered beyond repair. Shattered memories, dignity, relationships, the time caring for a loved one is completely gone. The family tries to put the pieces back together again but it will never be the same.

At a time when Helen Sophie Kroll-Mullard should have been able to enjoy grandkids and great-grandkids, introducing the new generations to her wisdom and zest for life, Alzheimer's clouded her memory. Instead of the strength of the family, she became dependant on those who were now her caretakers.

My sister Emily and I took early retirement to care for our mother. Her life became our life. When her care required that someone be awake 24 hours a day to keep her safe from herself, we finally had to move her to a nursing home. It removed some of the stress from the families but also created new ones. She never became mean or violent, but we could feel her frustration, and we cried that this once amazing woman was reduced to so meager an existence.

Her sister and their mother, my grandmother, also suffered from Alzheimer's disease. I do not like my odds...

More than 7 out of 10 people with Alzheimer's disease live at home, where almost 75% of their care is provided by family and friends.

Almost 10 million Americans are caring for a person with Alzheimer's or another dementia. Approximately one out of three of these caregivers is 60 years or older.

Shattered Memories, Shattered Lives

Shattered

30" x 30"
Karen Musgrave
Naperville, Illinois

Karen makes quilts and masks, gives presentations and workshops, curates and judges, and has dedicated her life to using quilt making to change the world. She works for The Alliance for American Quilts in several different capacities and curated an exhibit of Gee's Bend Quilts in Georgia, Armenia, and Kazakhstan.

Shattered

Alzheimer's is a horrible, dreadful disease. The body stays but the loved one disappears. My mother-in-law, Dorothy, has it. She is dying the death she most feared—the death of her mother. Fortunately she no longer remembers that fear. But then again, she remembers no one.

My mother-in-laws arms are crossed and shattered on this quilt. The hands of my husband, son, and myself are lovingly open and reaching out. I wished this made a difference, I pray it does. However, it is difficult to know, since she no longer remembers who we are. It is not easy, this long good-bye.

As Alzheimer's disease progresses, communication can become increasingly challenging. The memories of an Alzheimer's patient fade with each passing day. Sensitive and ongoing communication, however, is important, no matter how difficult it may become or how confused the person may appear.

Visits from loved ones are easily forgotten from one day to the next. Seeing friends and family may not rekindle joys from the past, but rather blank stares. It's at these difficult moments that we gather the strength to go on, remembering that the emotions expressed to those we love may be more important than what is actually being said.

What If I Can't Remember That I Loved You?

33" x 33"
Susan Gourley
Fort Wayne, Indiana

Susan's artwork ranges from quilts to wearable art, all using her own surface designed fabrics as her way of expressing herself. Her background is a fine arts major in painting and sculpture with a strong fiber arts history. She devotes herself full time to home schooling her children and her studio work.

There is deep sadness and loss held in the heart of those of us who have a loved one with this disease. In my case, it is my mother and two aunts. I express this loss with words and images, past and present. Some are on the surface; others are on the pressed cotton pieces that look like they float on the surface and, like memories, can fall away at any time and disappear. The sunset fills the background as the day ends, like the recollections of that day and the past.

Around the outside of the quilt I have written questions any mother would ask if faced with the loss of the most precious memories of motherhood:

To my dear child,
What if I can not remember the soft touch of your hand?
What happens when I do not know your smile?
What if I do not know my face as I see it in the mirror?
What about when there are no memories for
the day as the sun says its final goodbye?
What if I can not remember that I loved
the warm smell of the top of your head?
What if I will never remember
I held you in my arms as you slept?
What if I never again have the chance
to remember who I was
and who you were to me?
What if I can not remember that I loved you?

Finding a treatment that could delay onset by five years could reduce the number of people with Alzheimer's disease by nearly 50 percent after 50 years.

What If I Can't Remember...

Alzheimer's Thief

32½" x 35"
Sonia M. Callahan
Piedmont, California

Sonia, a mother of four, has lived and worked in many different places, including Australia, Indonesia, and England. She credits traveling for her love of ethnic fabrics, which she uses in most of her quilts. Her quilts have appeared in several publications, and an article she authored on cyanotype was published in *The American Quilter*. Her interest in quilting began when she helped immigrant students use their needle skills to subsidize their incomes. She is a most versatile teacher, having taught pre-school to community college and everything in between.

This quilt is a statement about the loss of abilities, debilitations and personality changes that can occur when a person is afflicted with Alzheimer's. Without advanced notice, the Alzheimer's Thief whittles away at abilities to remember, to make decisions, and to learn new tasks. At the same time, the thief steals initiative, mood stability, short term recall, task and place orientation, as well as abstract thinking. The thief selects and steals memory and brain functions that are required for independent living.

In the quilt one easily identifies the thief, running to places unknown, carrying his bowl of stolen goods. The background of the quilt was chosen because it resembles the specific pattern of tangles that are seen in slides of Alzheimer's altered brain tissue.

I dedicate this quilt to my mother, an Alzheimer's patient, who managed to communicate love to all those around her until almost the end.

Scientists believe that the changes in the brain that cause Alzheimer's disease begin 10 to 20 years before symptoms appear.

Alzheimer's Thief

Silent Tears

33½" x 48½"
Philomena Mudd
Louisville, Kentucky

Philomena made her first quilt in 1972. After years as a speech therapist she became a massage therapist and then began studying quilting. Now Philomena works exclusively from her home studio as massage therapist and "Promising Quilt Artist." She lives happily with her husband of 34 years and three well-loved rescued dogs.

My quilt is made in honor of my kind, gentle mother-in-law Mary Wohlleb. I've been married to her loving son Michael for 34 years. My sisters-in-law Moira, Rose, Chris, and Angie were all an intimate part of this project. We spent many hours together agonizing over pictures, poems, words, etc. Our grieving and sorrow were eased by the times together around the quilt.

The vertical aspect of the quilt roughly portrays the prison bars that increasingly trapped Mary and our family as we watched the many baffling aspects of Alzheimer's manifest. I used narrow lines of vertical quilting throughout the piece. They speak to how confined Mom's life had become as her disease progressed. The pictures, words, and leaves appear to swirl around an empty center, reminding me of the void that Alzheimer's presents in the lives of all of us connected to this disease.

Mary experienced this void initially as extreme frustration with herself and her failing memory. She would smack her hand and make disparaging remarks about herself. The tragic part of those early years of this disease was knowing that she knew, as we did, what the future would hold.

Stanzas from *Is It I?* by Donna Pucciani are written on the leaves. Donna's mother-in law, Mary Bostock, died of Alzheimer's 10 years ago.

In a Gallup poll commissioned by the Alzheimer's Association, 1 in 10 Americans said that they had a family member with Alzheimer's and 1 in 3 knew someone with the disease.

Silent Tears

The Left Behind

38" x 60"
Claudia Comay
San Ramon, California

Claudia joyfully focuses on shape by using fabric in a minimalist way. She exhibits throughout the United States and internationally. She received an artist in-residence fellowship to Yosemite National Park and was featured in the PBS video *Woman's Work: Making Quilts—Creating Art*.

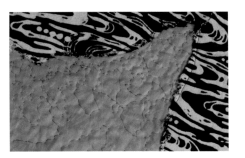

I began this quilt shortly after the death of my cousin, a young woman in her thirties. I was angry about her sad and lonely passing and I was of mixed feelings about how her father (my mother's brother) would react to her death. He had been diagnosed with Alzheimer's for more than a year by then. I remember several conversations with my aunt (his main caregiver) in which we wondered if the disease was a blessing in disguise at this difficult time.

This was a very hard time for me. As I cuddled my infant girl, I remember thinking about the injustice of seeing your child die while at the same time having your husband pass through your life like sand through your fingers, unable to grasp and share the grief.

It was with this hopeless despair and anger that I began my quilt. Subsequently my mother's sister was diagnosed with Alzheimer's. I felt fragile and fearful, and I put the quilt away. When I could finally deal with my emotions, I imbued the quilt with all the anger within me at the injustice of it all. Now there are only tears left.

With Alzheimer's disease it is normal to feel profound loss. It can be the same emotion as when someone dies. It's natural to mourn the person and feel anger. It is helpful to talk with someone you trust about your grief and try to accept things that are beyond your control.

The Left Behind

TRAVEL GOLF BRIDGE DINE
PAINT READ GARDEN
DRIVE WRITE SING
MIX⋄MINGLE LAUGH
SIGN PRINT FIND
TIE BUTTON ZIP
BRUSH COMB SMILE
WALK HUG TALK
SWALLOW
BREATHE

She's Come Undone

34½" x 44"
Gay Young Ousley
San Angelo, Texas

Gay constructs colorful fabric landscapes that reflect her love of nature and her appreciation of the majestic scenery of West Texas and the American Southwest. Her work has been shown at the Museum of Western Art in Wickenburg, Arizona; the Fiber Arts Fiesta in Albuquerque, New Mexico; and numerous regional shows in South Central Texas.

My mother has Alzheimer's disease. There are not enough words in any language to describe how devastating that is. Alzheimer's takes a neat, orderly life and unravels it, piece by piece. The shutdown of the brain is agonizing, leaving an empty shell where once a personality thrived. Finally, even involuntary movements become impossible and the patient is gone with no way left to say goodbye.

The red letters on my quilt spell out verbs expressing interests, abilities, and life functions, taken away by Alzheimer's, one by one, until nothing is left. They are fused with raw edges left to fray with time. Alzheimer's leaves lots of raw, frayed edges—in the patient, of course, but also in the lives of family members, friends, and caregivers. Alzheimer's disease is not pretty. Quilting stitches meander. My mother does a lot of meandering, both physically and mentally, as the disease continues.

A braid of hand-dyed silk ribbon unravels, like the life that unravels before our very eyes. As the disease continues, the braid gets looser and thinner until it can no longer hold together.

Alzheimer's disease puts us all at risk. There is much left to discover towards finding a cure. I hope we get there soon...

Statistics from Alzheimer's disease International (ADI) show 24.3 million people worldwide currently have dementia from Alzheimer's disease and all other causes, and 4.6 million more develop it every year. The total number will nearly double every 20 years, to 42.3 million in 2020 and 81.1 million in 2040.

She's Come Undone

The Crooked Path

33½" x 35½"
Diane Petersmarck
Evanston, Illinois

Diane is a scrap booker turned art quilter—a natural progression as both involve design and color. It is obvious from Diane's work that this new fabric medium has been eagerly embraced! She began small, with fiber postcards, and has now graduated to wall quilts that are thoroughly enchanting.

The path traveled by Alzheimer's victims is long and crooked. It gets narrower and narrower as time passes.

After moving through some of the stages of grief, I now accept what is happening to Dad. It still makes me very sad, but I just want to be with him for as long as I am able, until he crosses that portal into a world that I can not share. The subtitle of this quilt (if there was one) would be, "Daddy, let me hold your hand as you walk the crooked path."

I feel a tiny glimmer of joy (yes, joy) sometimes when I'm with Dad and I experience one of those few-and-far-between moments when he "comes back" to us. Like when I was sitting on his bed the other night and hugged and kissed him and told him I loved him and he hugged me back and said, "I love you too, Diane." In his stage of Alzheimer's, that show of reciprocal emotion doesn't happen all that often, especially not combined with his recognition of me as his daughter.

So, while much of our time together is frustrating and exhausting, I am thankful for these few moments of joy. I will continue to spend as much time as I can with him, holding his hand as he walks the crooked path.

The stages of grief don't happen neatly or in order. They can't be rushed or planned for. Family members of those afflicted with Alzheimer's move in and out of the different stages as time goes on. These stages include denial, anger, guilt, and finally, acceptance.

The Crooked Path

The Song Goes On

35" x 35"
Janet M. Heliker
Waterloo, Nebraska

Janet is a "try something new" type. She married her high school sweetheart, the engineer, and raised five interesting, diverse people. She graduated from college at 42 with a master's degree in economics. After 18 years of teaching high school, she found the wonderful world of quilting and the joy of spending time with her 13 grandchildren.

Alzheimer's, unfortunately, has become a part of our family. My mother-in-law, Esther, and my mother, Irene, both suffered from the disease in their final years. As their caregivers, we were witness to their sad, lonely decline.

A purse and its contents tell a lot about the woman who carried them. The contents of this purse, strewn along the path of Alzheimer's, are the pieces of life, forgotten and lost. Objects farthest from the purse are the first things forgotten. Objects closest to the purse are not lost until the later stages of the disease.

The purse is lined with music, the one thing that remained with both women to the end. Esther could play the piano into the late stages of the disease, and Mom enjoyed singing along. The song flows out of the purse at death and into the horizon—a new beginning through eternal life with God.

This quilt resolved some of the grief that Alzheimer's created in my life. It has allowed me to think through loss and has given me the opportunity to commit myself to the peace of knowing that both of the women I love are now singing in heaven with the angels, restored in spirit.

Many caregivers report their loved ones still being able to sing long after most verbal communication has left them. Perhaps music resides in a part of the brain less affected by the disease. Music therapy can help enrich the lives of people with Alzheimer's disease. It stirs memories, emotions, and can encourage group activity.

The Song Goes On

I'm Going Home Now

37" x 40"
Linda Carlson
Mexico, Missouri

Linda has been teaching quilting for more than 25 years, throughout the United States and overseas. Her specialties are needle-turn hand appliqué and precision machine piecing techniques. Linda is the author of four books and enjoys sharing her heartfelt belief that quilts have the ability to soothe the stresses of our every day lives. Linda is also a fabric designer for Benartex fabric.

My dear mother-in-law's last years were exactly how she prayed they would not be: coping with Alzheimer's. When Doretta Carlson visited her daughter for Sunday dinner, she would say, "I want to go home." Jean and Stan Parker asked if she meant the facility where she lived, but that wasn't right. "Do you mean the house on 79th Street? The Benson senior apartments on Military? Your apartment at New Cassel?" No, those weren't right either.

The night before Doretta passed, Jean and Stan visited her. Doretta was excited, her eyes sparkling. When Jean asked how she was, she answered with a big smile, "I'm going home now! Mom and Sis are waiting for me."

In the middle of the night, Doretta went home; to Mom and Sis, Fritz, the father-in-law I never knew, and her four brothers. Her last night on earth was a miracle. For the past few years, Doretta had great difficulty forming coherent thoughts, let alone complete sentences.

The Seminole patchwork behind the photo-transfers of Doretta's homes is the lap quilt I made for her in 1988, a gift she caressed with loving but confused hands until she "went Home" on January 3, 1999.

Wanting to "go home" is very common among Alzheimer's patients. They may attempt to leave home simply because they forget they are home. Or, they know there was a time when things were easier to understand and day-to-day tasks were less frustrating. They want to go back to the way things were… "home." Going home doesn't necessarily mean a physical location; it often refers to a state of mind.

I'm Going Home Now

Sylvia—A Life's Journey

34" x 30"
Gail Garber
Albuquerque, New Mexico

Gail began quilting 26 years ago after taking a class at a local shop. Now internationally known, she teaches and lectures throughout the United States and abroad. She is the author of two books: *Stellar Journeys* and *Sensational Stars*, and is known for her colorful, geometric, free-form designs.

Although Sylvia, my Mom, has not yet been diagnosed with Alzheimer's, she does suffer from dementia.

Her quilted journey began as a young bride, her portrait painted from a photograph taken on her wedding day. The first third of the quilt is rosy and full of joy with the brilliant colors of sunrise.

The middle section is more muted. The births of her six children are represented in a spiraling row of flying geese. Although this was a happy time, it was financially difficult for my parents.

The colors in the last third are dark and stormy, for the period following my father's death when her memory faded. She had to leave her family home and move to New Mexico to be nearer to two of her daughters, leaving most of her possessions behind.

Bright points remain. The red shooting-star points are my joy in being able to be close to my mother in her last years, although the unquilted black void of dementia threatens to take even that from me. Mom was the rock upon which we depended as children, and is now the colorful thread that is woven into our adult lives.

In 2005, Alzheimer's Disease International (ADI) reported that a new case of dementia arises every seven seconds, worldwide. The ADI is working with the Alzheimer's Association and other members worldwide to raise the profile of dementia and to call governments to action.

Sylvia—A Life's Journey

A Tribute To A Man And His Family

32½" x 38"
Marla Ferguson
Palisade, Colorado

Marla began sewing when she was 10 and has been quilting for the past 21 years. She started out with strip-pieced traditional quilts and has grown to include fusible applique. When she found out that she could combine quilting and garments in wearable art, she was in heaven! Wearable art is still her favorite sewing/quilting venue. Marla loves working with color, design, fabric and embellishments and has a current focus working on art quilts. She especially enjoys making some kind of statement or interpreting a theme with her quilts and wearables. She loves to support worthy causes by providing quilts for fund-raising auctions and sales. It allows her to feed her own soul through the creative process while providing for the healing of others. Marla has won awards for her wearable art both locally and nationally.

In 2004, when Daryl and I wed, we had each been previously married and both of our fathers had recently passed. Instead of wedding gifts, we asked for donations to hospice in memory of my father, and to the Alzheimer's Association in memory of Daryl's father.

This quilt is a tribute to a Daryl's father, a man whom I never met, and to his family who has opened their hearts to me. By allowing me to share my father-in-law's battle with Alzheimer's, it is my hope to inspire others to learn more about the disease and to know that, sadly, they are not alone.

Photographs of Daryl's father were transferred to fabric and layered on the quilt. They are bright at the top, but gradually become gray and dark towards the bottom of the quilt. Puzzle pieces have been cut from them, at first revealing bright fabric beneath. Gradually the cuts go deeper, exposing batting. Finally the cuts go through all three layers, creating holes of lost memories. The excised puzzle pieces dangle at the bottom of the quilt as a reminder of all that has been lost.

Alzheimer's takes away the memories of a lifetime, little by little, until there is literally nothing left.

Every 72 seconds, someone in America develops Alzheimer's disease. By mid-century, someone will develop Alzheimer's disease every 11 seconds.

A Tribute To A Man...

Once A Shining Star

36" x 36"
Helen Marshall
Waikanae, New Zealand

Helen has been quilting and embroidering for many years. She teaches widely throughout New Zealand and internationally as well. Helen curates the *New Zealand Quilts for the World Quilt Shows* in the USA. A faculty member of QuiltUniversity.com, Helen is the author of two books, *The Miniature Embroidered Quilt* and *Wheel of Mystery Quilts: Surprising Designs from a Classic Block.*

My mother had Alzheimer's. She was the first woman accountancy graduate at Canterbury University in New Zealand, and although she did not practice after my brother and I were born, she was always involved in community fund-raising and served on committees of national charity organizations. She was very intelligent, a great bridge player, and had a wide circle of interesting friends. The onset of her Alzheimer's saddened me so very much. It took so much away from her.

I used an old traditional block called Memory Star, very appropriate, I think. I drafted a ring of forget-me-not flowers (the symbol of Alzheimer's here in New Zealand) onto the block. The rest of the block is shaded from bright to dull as a reminder of the downhill effect this disease has on people.

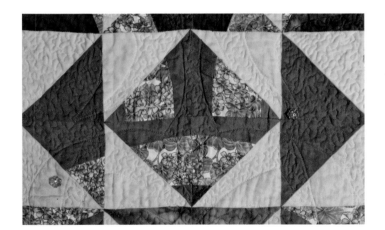

The quilting has a section of meandering pattern, one of the symptoms of the mind and body when this disease takes over, and there are some forget-me not beads scattered over the quilt to emphasis the "not knowing where they are" that effects patients.

I found making this quilt was very emotional for me.

It is common for a person with dementia to wander and become lost. Over 60 percent of those with dementia will wander at some point. Wandering is obviously dangerous for the person with Alzheimer's and stressful for caregivers and family. The Alzheimer's Association Safe Return® program is a nationwide identification, support, and registration program that provides assistance when a person with Alzheimer's or related dementia wanders and becomes lost locally or far from home.

Once A Shining Star

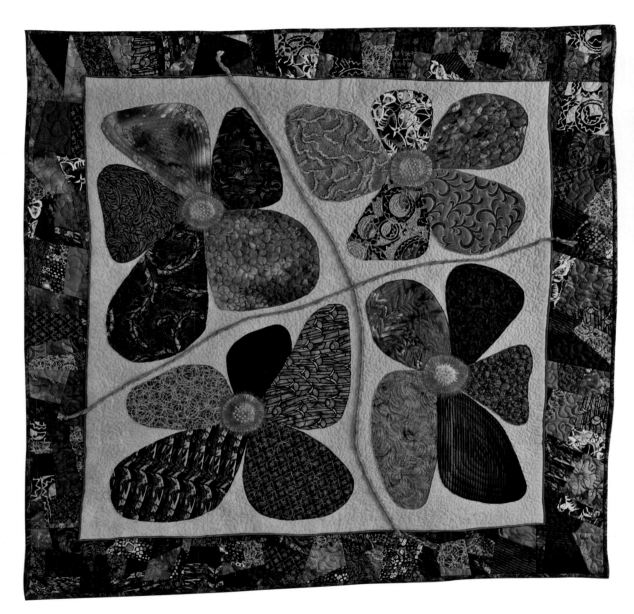

Violets For Irene

38" x 38"
Mary Andrews
Grand Blanc, Michigan

Mary has been a quilt artist for almost 20 years. Taught to sew by her mother as a child, Mary sewed clothing for herself and her children then began sewing quilts. Her award-winning quilts have traveled all over the world and are in several public collections.

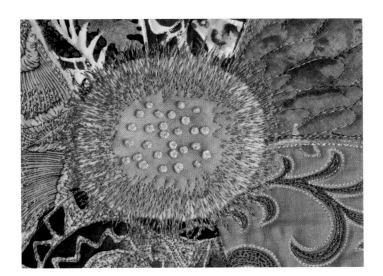

Irene was my mother. She has always been my inspiration and my personal coach. Although she passed away almost 30 years ago, her words of encouragement have kept me going with my art, even when other things in life have distracted me. There wasn't a label for the dementia that took over her mind back then. I was told it was "hardening of the arteries." It was very hard to watch this very creative, vibrant woman lose her ability to do the things in life that she loved so much. If this disease is hereditary, I surely hope they find a cure during my lifetime, which is why I made this quilt and want to be a part of bringing people the awareness that research is needed to find a cure.

Purple was her favorite color and violets her favorite flower. She had beautiful African violets in every window. When I decided to do a tribute to her, purple violets were the first thing to pop into my mind. She always saved the scraps from every project to use somewhere else so I made each petal a different fabric. I didn't have the right color for the background so I dyed a piece the color I needed along with the cording. The scrappy "crazy-patch" border represents the craziness of the dementia that surrounded her later in her life. Even though the craziness exists, there is beauty. We can still see the inner beauty of the flower even if it is only in our memory.

There is no one diagnostic test that can detect if a person has Alzheimer's disease. The process involves several different kinds of tests. Diagnostic tools and criteria make it possible for physicians to make a diagnosis of Alzheimer's with an accuracy of about 90 percent. It is only confirmed by autopsy.

Violets For Irene

Forever Flowers

32" x 30"
Janet Jones Worley
Huntsville, Alabama

Janet is a professional quilt artist, designer, author, and teacher. Her newest book is *Quilts for Ice Cream Lovers*. She has appeared on *Simply Quilts* with Alex Anderson (HGTV), *The Morning Show*, and *Global View* (Canadian television). Janet is the creator of the irresistible Quilters With Attitude soft-sculpture lapel pins. One of her quilts is on permanent display in the library of Peking, China.

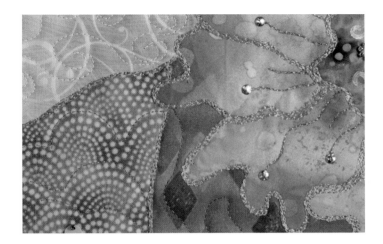

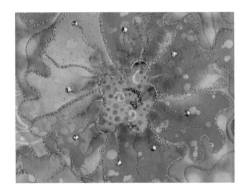

I designed this one-of-a-kind quilt in honor of my mother-in-law, Mary Knowles Worley. Flowers have always given her such pleasure. Thankfully they still do. Sometimes, even with Alzheimer's, when Mary looks at a flower, a glimpse of that joy shines through.

I began by drawing a single fanciful blossom and then added others in various sizes. Choosing the color was the simplest part of the process, since I knew it must be in Mary's favorite shades of pink. As the design progressed, I developed a new appliqué technique. Hand painting, hand beading, and machine beading were used on the petals to get just the right shades. The end result... a bouquet of "Forever Flowers"... unforgettable.

I wanted to create a quilt that would capture and express the joy in Mary's life. It's very important to me that the effects of this disease do not over-shadow the zest and enjoyment for life she once had. When people see my quilt, I hope it brings back the memories of happy times to everyone, not letting the disease have the ultimate victory.

Many Alzheimer's caregivers have expressed how this devastating disease robs their loved one of their personality. As the disease progresses, memories fade, one by one, beyond the control of the individual with Alzheimer's. One of the few things that caregivers can control, however, is choosing to remember the good times, remembering their loved ones when they were healthy.

Forever Flowers

A Day With Beebe

32" x 45"
Marsha McCloskey
Eugene, Oregon
Quilted by Sheila Snyder

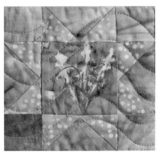

Marsha is one of the quilting world's best-known authors and teachers. She has written or co-authored more than 20 books on quiltmaking since 1981. Specializing in traditional designs, such as the Feathered Star, she has taught drafting, rotary cutting, and machine piecing to quilters all over the United States and in eight foreign countries. She has her own small publishing company, Feathered Star Productions, and has designed lines of quilting fabric for In the Beginning-Fabrics and Clothworks.

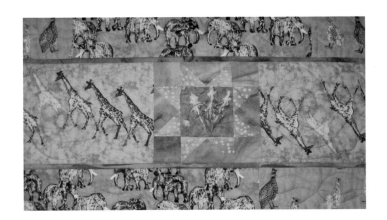

I have long held that using someone else's pattern, or copying an antique quilt, gives one insight into that person's creative process. I asked my friend to send me what she had left of a fabric line her mom designed a few years before being diagnosed with Alzheimer's. Using Beebe's fabric was, as I had hoped, like spending the day with her.

The fabrics are whimsical and quirky. Dandelions and giraffes, elephants, and guinea hens are on the march—intrepid travelers, painted with broad strokes. The fabrics and Beebe told me what to do. I had a good day.

Midway through the sewing, though, I lost a bright green square. The piece was not to be found, so I replaced it with a dull gray one. Then the next large piece was somehow sewn on upside down, and I just left it that way. The gray square and the gray border are for "forgetfulness" and memories lost.

"All those moments will be lost, in time, like tears in rain."

—Roy, in the movie Blade Runner

It has been just over one hundred years since Alois Alzheimer first described the disease that would later bear his name. His patient was a 51-year-old woman who was disoriented, had difficulty putting words together, and experienced severe short term memory loss. She said, "I have lost myself."

A Day With Beebe

Mourning Too Soon

30" x 32"
Diane Gaudynski
Waukesha, Wisconsin

Diane is an NQA Master Quilter, has won numerous prestigious national and international awards and authored two best-selling books on machine quilting, *Guide to Machine Quilting* and *Quilt Savvy—Gaudynski's Machine Quilting Guidebook.* Known for her traditional, intricate, and original designs in home-machine quilting, she is a patient teacher to machine quilters around the country.

Using somber colors suitable for Victorian latter-stage mourning dresses, I chose silk dupioni fabric for this classic strippy-style quilt to create a quilted elegy. It signifies the sadness we feel at the loss of our loved ones too soon because of Alzheimer's disease.

The flowing vines are cut short at the top and bottom, much like Alzheimer's will cut short lives. The quilting motifs are original, and most are freehand, done in silk thread with wool batting on my home sewing machine, a Bernina 730.

The Mourning Dove, the central image, emits its haunting cry of loss amid leaves and feathers lightly touched by end-of-year color, and its cry is echoed in our minds when all of us are affected by this disease. I made this to commemorate those I know who suffer from this disease, and also for the caregivers whose patience, love, and caring is a testament to the depth of human compassion.

Scientists around the world are trying to learn more about Alzheimer's. There are more than 50 compounds being tested to treat Alzheimer's and nearly every major pharmaceutical company is working on this problem, as are private organizations, and the federal government. Research is focusing on better ways to diagnose, control, reverse, and prevent Alzheimer's disease.

Mourning Too Soon

Jackie's Chocolate Quilt

36" x 37"
Joan Hailey Hansen
Rolla, Missouri

JACKIE SAID, "ALWAYS KEEP A POSITIVE ATTITUDE"

Jackie was smart, vivacious, pretty and one of the most popular girls in school. Her greatest fear was that she would get Alzheimer's disease like her mother. We weren't sure if she knew she was sick because she often said "I am so glad that I didn't get that old Alzheimer's. We must keep a positive attitude." It robbed her of her memory, and the ability to care for herself, but it never robbed her of her spirit.

JACKIE VOSS JONES 1931–2006

Joan, an accomplished stitcher of wearable art, has recently turned her attention to wall quilts. Her pieces are filled with detail and often tell a story. She recently discovered the joy of portrait painting on cloth. This is the first time she has exhibited a quilt nationally.

I went to high school with Jackie Voss Jones. She called herself a "chocoholic." (The best thing you could give her was a box of chocolates.) She was vivacious, witty, popular, and involved. Everyone knew Jackie and loved her. She worked hard to run her farm and raise her children. Her son married my daughter, and we shared a precious granddaughter, Hallie Baxter Jones.

Jackie's life wasn't easy, but she never felt sorry for herself. Her mother and mother-in-law both suffered from Alzheimer's disease and getting it was Jackie's greatest fear. When she was diagnosed, she couldn't remember and often told me, "Aren't you glad we didn't get that old Alzheimer's?" Then she would add, "Mother said we must always have a positive attitude," and she carefully enunciated the word, "pos-i-tive."

Jackie's symptoms robbed her of the ability to care for herself, and finally it took her away from her beloved farm. Through it all, she always knew her family and maintained a sunny disposition. Jackie also had cancer, which eventually caused her death. She kept her "pos-i-tive" attitude to the end.

I have *hope* that one day we can eradicate this cruel disease known as Alzheimer's, and like Jackie said, **we must keep a positive attitude!**

Although there is currently no cure for Alzheimer's, new treatments are on the horizon as a result of accelerating insight into the biology of the disease. Research has also shown that effective care and support can improve quality of life for individuals and their caregivers over the course of the disease from diagnosis to the end of life.

Jackie's Chocolate Quilt

Research Now...There's Still Time

30" x 44"
Nancy Brenan Daniel
Prescott, Arizona

Nancy is a traditional and a studio quilt maker, designer and teacher. As the granddaughter of a quilter she has had a lifelong interest in the art. After the university she began her professional life as an art educator. Today, she is a skilled designer and teacher, as well as a prolific author of books and magazine articles — mostly about the art of the quilt.

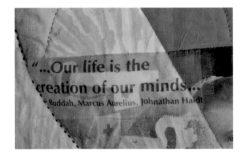

I am a lucky daughter. In my mother's 90th and 91st years, we had a lot of time to visit and talk of many things — mostly family things, and funny things, and our lives together. We were very lucky to have had that time, and for Mom to be fully rational.

Sometime after her 90th birthday party, she phoned me with an urgent request to visit. She was worried about something. She wanted to talk right away. I settled in for a bombshell.

"I've misplaced my stamps. I haven't been able to find them all day," she said. "Do you think I have 'Early Onset Dementia?'" She was **totally** serious. She no sooner said the words than she remembered where she had hidden the stamps.

"Mom," I said, "At your age, I don't think anything could be called 'Early Onset!'" Five seconds passed before the two of us broke into uncontrolled, tear-producing laughter. We were the lucky ones. We had each other, totally, until the day she crossed over the Rainbow Bridge to be with Dad and her lifelong collection of dogs and friends who were there waiting for her.

This quilt is dedicated to **research**—and those who do the research. I hope that soon all daughters and sons, grandchildren and spouses will have their loved ones totally present until it is their time to leave this earth.

In the past people believed memory loss was a normal part of aging, often regarding even Alzheimer's as natural age-related decline. Experts now recognize severe memory loss as a symptom of serious illness.

Research Now...

Fade To Gray

38" x 40"
Melody Crust
Kent, Washington

Melody is a nationally recognized, award-winning quilter active in every facet of quilting: teaching, curating, judging, exhibiting, and writing. Her quilts are bold, jubilant, and sumptuously embellished. Melody is the author of two books, *A Fine Line* and *Quilt Toppings: Fun and Fancy Embellishment Techniques*.

As an artist, I am always enveloped in color. Every minute of every day is about glorious reds, warm, rich browns, the thrill of that perfect shade of purple, and the myriad shades of green. I love them all.

Alzheimer's is about losing life's colors — words evaporate from vocabularies, memories that define us and enrich our lives fade and disappear. Yet the human spirit is resilient and our capacity to hope for a better tomorrow persists. I quilted that "hope" with bright threads over the surface of the quilt.

"Fade to Gray's" red binding represents the love and generosity surrounding Alzheimer's patients and their families, as whole communities work together to find a cure.

Age, family history, and heredity are all risk factors we can't change. Research is beginning to reveal clues about other risk factors we may be able to influence.

Head injury: There appears to be a strong link between serious head injury and future risk of Alzheimer's. Protect your head by buckling your seat belt, wearing your helmet when participating in sports, and "fall-proofing" your home.

Heart-head connection: Some of the strongest evidence links brain health to heart health. The risk of developing Alzheimer's or vascular dementia appears to be increased by many conditions that damage the heart or blood vessels, including high blood pressure, heart disease, stroke, and diabetes.

General healthy aging: Other lines of evidence suggest that strategies for overall healthy aging may help keep the brain healthy and may even offer some protection against developing Alzheimer's or related diseases. Try to keep your weight within recommended guidelines, avoid tobacco and excess alcohol, stay socially connected, and exercise both your body and mind.

Fade To Gray

A Bouquet For You

33" x 33"
Sue Nickels
Ann Arbor, Michigan

Sue uses machine appliqué and machine quilting techniques to create traditional quilts often based on a theme and inspired by antique folk art style quilts. Sue's most well-known quilt is *The Beatles Quilt* made with her sister Pat Holly. This quilt won the 1998 AQS Best of Show award and is in the collection of the Museum of the American Quilter's Society.

My family has not been touched by Alzheimer's, but I have seen friends take on the challenge of caregiving, acutely aware of the person their loved one used to be, grieving for what is already lost, and what is yet to be forgotten. I can imagine, too, the fear and sadness Alzheimer's patients must feel when they can contemplate the path their lives will take.

This bouquet is for you, for the wives and husbands, daughters and sons, sisters and brothers who care for family members with Alzheimer's. And it is for those who suffer with the confusion and fear that this disease brings.

My bouquet is framed with tears of sorrow for all that is lost, but bright with the promise of hope that some day very soon a cure will be found. Like the flowers gathered in my hand let us come together to make this happen.

The Alzheimer's Art Quilt Initiative has donated at least $2 from the sale of this book to Alzheimer's research. For more details, and to learn how you can help, please visit www.AlzQuilts.org.

A Bouquet For You

Index

Artists

Index

Quilt Title